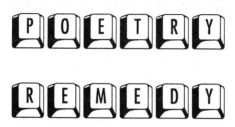

POETRY REMEDY

by Ann Kelley

The Hypatia Trust & Patten Press

Newmill

1999

Dedication: *To my husband, Dr. Robert Marshall, whose encouragement gave birth to the Poetry Remedy Project and whose unflagging enthusiasm has nurtured it.*

First published, 1999
©Ann Kelley
Cover illustration by Peter Bennett

ISBN 1 872229 29 8
Printed & bound by The Book Factory, London

Table of Contents

ACKNOWLEDGEMENTS

Special thanks to all the patients and carers who gave permission for the use of their writing: Jim McNalley, Jan Sherman and the rest of the staff at the Mental Health Day Care Centre of Boundervean, Camborne; the nurses, physios and occupational therapists at the Stroke and Rehabilitation Unit at City Hospital, Truro; Dr Deborah Stevens, Sister Teresa Finnegan and all the staff at St Julia's Hospice, St Michael's Hospital, Hayle, and Mark Sansom, Sally Condliffe and all the staff at Marie Therese House, Hayle.

Thanks to the Foundation for Sport and the Arts for their generous support of *Poetry Remedy*, providing us with funds to print poem posters and to make frames for them to hang in hospitals, hospices and surgeries in Cornwall in addition to helping us to publish this book.

Thanks to all the generous professional poets who provided poems for Poetry Remedy Posters in Hospitals. Special thanks to Lindsey Shaw Radley for much hard work designing the poem posters and printing them.

Thanks to our patrons : D. M. Thomas, Miroslav Holub, Sylvia Kantaris and Michael Galsworthy.

To all the brave and interesting people I have had the pleasure to meet in the Cornwall health care system over the past two years: patients, their families, friends and carers, nursing staff, volunteers, occupational therapists, physiotherapists, speech therapists, doctors and managers, thank you!

The editor gratefully acknowledges permission to reproduce the following copyright poems in this book: Patricia Heeney: 'Things I Like' from *Lifelines 2*, Town House & Country House Publishers; Derek Mahon: 'Absence' from *Light Music, Lifelines 2*, Town House & country House; Dick Davis: 'Six am Thoughts', *Lifelines 2*, Miroslav Holub: 'Open the Door' from *Poems Before and After*, Bloodaxe; Raymond Carver: 'Late Fragment' from *Lifelines 2*, Town House & Country House; Zofia Ilynska: 'I Talk to my Cancer' from *Address of Paradise*, Tabb House; John Cooper Clark: Haiku, from *Writing Poems*, Bloodaxe; Exercise: 'The Furniture Game' from *Writing Poems*, Bloodaxe Books.

Ann Kelley, January, 1999

FOREWORD

This book is both an account of some poetry workshops and a 'how to' book of ways of encouraging non-writers to produce a piece of creative work. There are about forty exercises with a step-by-step guide to the methods. In one sense, this book is a diary, interspersed with notes about the meeting of particular people on specific days, and the poetic work that emerged from those encounters. The exercises introduced in the following pages are not meant to be directives or a series which must be followed in an organised sequential way. The personal notes that I have made throughout the sections will make this even more clear; certain exercises will appeal for one situation, and others for different occasions.

So far I have worked with four different patient groups in Cornwall over a period of two years. This book is a personal account of how I have assisted ordinary people who, perhaps, have never tried to write creatively in any form or specifically to write poems. The groups I have worked with are those terminally ill at a hospice, patients who suffer with severe degenerative diseases (multiple sclerosis and motor neurone disease), mental health care out-patients who may be schizophrenic and severely depressed, as well as persons in a stroke and brain injury rehabilitation unit of a general hospital.

The poems are written at a time in all their lives when they are vulnerable, sick, and dependent on carers and hospital staff for most of their physical needs. The workshops, sometimes in groups, often one to one, help individuals to express hopes, to say their thanks to loved ones and to talk about their pain and fears. The workshops give them an opportunity to produce something they can be proud of. They are people before they are patients and have often lost the ability to do everyday things the rest of us take for granted like washing, dressing, making a cup of tea, going for a walk, enjoying a hobby or sport.

They are able to write about the people they were before they became ill. They know their skills and their deficits, they remember the things they enjoyed doing, the places and people they loved. Their lives are not over because they are ill. They still have lives to live.

In the case of brain damaged patients the actual exercise of trying to remember is helpful. Paralysed from strokes, they are encouraged to use their hands to write, and to remember words they have forgotten. The process of writing and crafting a poem is a therapy of sorts, as many professional writers will admit. For the anxious and depressed it can be a way through their unhappiness and empower them at a time when they need to feel they can still make something worth having. The resulting poems enable the medical staff and carers and families to have a deeper insight into their patients' lives and problems, their wishes and fears.

Mental patients and people with learning difficulties gain a feeling of independence and satisfaction when they see their work in print. Often their own handwriting is not up to much and they may be anxious about spelling words. They are happy to be led through the process of poem making and to make a worthwhile piece of lasting work. I encourage them to write and write and write and never mind about the spelling. I can correct that for them with their permission. My job is not to get them to produce a work of art, necessarily, but to show them the they can create a short piece of work and make a poem: real poetry by real people.

Introduction

The idea was born in 1995. Several like-minded people — my husband, Dr Robert Marshall, consultant histopathologist at Royal Cornwall Hospitals Trust, Lindsey Shaw-Radley, medical secretary, and D M Thomas, the novelist and poet who lives in Truro and I — thought it would be a good idea to introduce poetry into hospitals and health care settings in Cornwall. We wanted to see poems on the walls in waiting rooms, clinics and other public areas, for the benefit of staff, patients and visitors.

Poems on the Underground (a London-based organisation) very kindly started us off with a gift of seventy poem posters, which we laminated and gave to wards and health centres. This was soon after followed up by a grant from the Foundation for Sport and the Arts, to print our own poem posters and have them properly framed. I wrote to about forty published poets and asked them to give suitable poems for the hospitals. There was a good response from some well-known writers like Carol Ann Duffy and Benjamin Zephaniah, Miroslav Holub and Alan Ross, and we also chose favourite old poems to go up on the walls. From this seeding, *Poetry Remedy* was born and the child is doing well.

The next step was to get patients and carers to write poetry. Personally I am not a therapist or a counsellor or a medic of any sort. My own work is in writing and photography and my published work includes short stories, magazine articles, novels, a book of photographs and a recorded audio book about cats. I began writing poetry eleven years ago after my son died. I found the actual process and craft of writing poems, the discipline of it, was therapeutic. It helped me say things I had not been able to put into words before. Some of the poems have been published in literary and poetry magazines, and a collection was shortlisted for a national prize.

I approached several hospital consultants with the workshop idea but could not interest them. Then, by chance, I met two schizophrenics who were at a poetry reading held by a group call 'Survivors', which took place after a meeting about schizophrenia at Treliske Hospital, Truro. I talked to these two about the idea of starting workshops and they both were very keen. They suggested that I might come to their mental health day care centre, Boundervean, in Camborne, and run workshops with them there. So I met with their manager and began work as a volunteer, helping users of the centre to write and think poetically.

At Boundervean there is a regular group of about seven people with whom I have been working since 1995, although occasionally one or two of them are too ill to attend. There is one very anxious woman who always starts off saying 'I can't do that' whatever I suggest, but she always produces something and often quite a lot. The group consists of people who are diagnosed schizophrenic, manic depressive, some who have attempted suicide, patients who suffer from cerebral palsy and others with mental health difficulties. One man is partially sighted. These make up our 'club'.

In August of 1996 I started with a second group at the Rehabilitation Unit for stroke and head injury patients at the City Hospital, Truro. The occupational therapists and speech therapists were keen to have me, and after a stern reminder that patient privacy was paramount, I began working with chosen patients once a week. This is sometimes a difficult group. Often the writers cannot physically write. So I need to scribe for them as they dictate to me or another helper. If I can get a carer or visiting relation to help I do, and ask these helpers to join in on the writing as well.

This rehabilitation group benefits from the challenge to their hurt brains, and often, even as a non-medical person, I can see an improvement in their motor skills and memory during the weeks and months I work with them. At the least, creative writing relieves the boredom of being in hospital. At best, it gives them the satisfaction of having produced something. Each session is a challenge for me, too, as I never know how many writers there will be, what their skills are or even if they will be able to speak. Can they remember anything?

Words may be, and usually are, elusive to them and they need help to find the right words again. This particular group is often quite emotional, and seem constantly on the edge of sorrow and grief. One of the writers in this group, an ex-nurse, tells me that

10

it is the left-side affected stroke victims who get emotional, as she herself does at the slightest excuse. Other problems get aired in these sessions and I encourage people to put it all down on paper. A constructive example of this was one young man who found himself unable to keep a promise to a very sick bed-neighbour. He wrote about it, then the poem was sent to the lad in question. Hopefully, both men benefited from the exchange of feeling.

The next group I established was at Marie Therese House, a unit at St Michael's Hospital, Hayle, which gives respite care to sufferers of severe degenerative diseases like multiple sclerosis (MS) and motor neurone disease. This is a wonderful group, very keen to produce a poem each time. They are people who often have failing physical and mental abilities and they are delighted to be able to create something. I am from outside — not primarily concerned with their physical health — and I, as their 'writing teacher' as opposed to carer, can encourage them to write about their fears and anxieties.

My latest poet-recruits are at St Julia's Hospice, Hayle. I go there once a week or more if necessary, and if anyone wants to write a letter, dictate their life story, hear some poetry or write a poem I help them do it. I met a woman at the hospice on Christmas Eve. She was waiting for an ambulance to take her for treatment at West Cornwall Hospital, Penzance. I suggested that she might like to write something to help relieve the tedium and stress of waiting. She had been ill since she was seventeen with cancer and she was now forty-one. She agreed, probably to avoid hurting my feelings. In the half an hour while she waited for the ambulance, she produced a love poem for her husband. She was so delighted with the result that she wanted to know if she could write another? How to go about it? What should she read? Could she work with me again?

I saw her a week later and she had produced four more poems.She carried on with a flood of work until she died. She felt good about being able to say things to her family. And now they have something of her which she specifically wanted them to have. Even though she had been ill for longer than she had been well, she was a person first. She wanted to leave something of herself, and not just images of her illness, behind.

11

I have been asked by staff who are trying to find funding for me to continue, "How do we evaluate what you are doing? What about audit?" I don't know the answer to that. Ask the people who attend the workshops, I suppose.

I

GENERAL NOTES ON ENCOURAGING PEOPLE TO WRITE POETRY

WHAT'S IN A NAME? Quite a lot actually. When encouraging people to even attend poetry workshops, the best advice is *NOT TO TELL THEM THEY ARE GOING TO WRITE POETRY.* Instead call it a Creative Writing Workshop, much less scary.

Most non-writers can be forgiven for thinking that poetry is for school, written by men long dead, clever men who knew about Greek Myths and used archaic words.

'Poetry is for wimps,' said one of my Boundervean group at her first workshop.

'I can't do it!' another anxious group member from Boundervean always says when I suggest a subject and then produces a perfectly good piece of work.

Poems are simply ways of telling the truth and distilling the truth of our emotions. We may think we are writing about a hobby or a memory, a dream or a garden, but something of the writer's 'soul' comes out in the chosen words and speaks to the reader.

The groups I work with have often never had the opportunity or inclination to write creatively. They are often in wheelchairs or confined to hospital beds, sometimes blind, or otherwise physically disabled and sometimes mentally disabled through illness or trauma. They might be bored, frustrated, angry, and full of fears. By showing them how to write a poem they are helped to express their thoughts and emotions. The fears, loves, hopes and precious memories they express are their own living memorial.

The other important rule when asking people to write a poem is to make the suggestion that they do not try to make it rhyme.

Why? Because the quest for rhyme detracts from the telling of truth. Later, when they are more experienced they can use half rhymes and full rhymes and they may want to play with various forms of poetry. I once made the mistake of criticising a man's first poem about his home because he had written it in rhyming verse and it sounded like a bit of doggerel. The whole heart of his experience had been sacrificed in his desire for a rhyme. He was of the school of thought that all poetry must rhyme. He did not return to a second workshop. Now I take care always to find something to praise in someone's first draft. If I cannot be encouraging then I keep quiet.

So, to start, simply try and write the truth.

Don't use rhyming words unless you are an experienced poet. (*Walker's Rhyming Dictionary* is a good source of words.)

Half rhymes are often better.

Be simple, be precise, discard cliché.

Be specific. Do not just say 'flower': which flower? which bird? which tree?

Do not generalise.

Do not preach to the readers.

Do not say you are sad, happy or angry. Show us through the story of the poem that you love or hate or grieve.

Do not try to be cleverer than you are: simplify.

Do not try to be 'poetic'. Do not use archaic words. 'Thou' and 'thee' and 'motes' are death to a good poem. They worked for dead poets, but not for you or me. Use modern expressions and words.

13

II

Notes for 'poets in residence'

1. Make sure there is a quiet room where you can hold the workshops.

Consider the following: Is there room for wheelchairs to be maneuvered if necessary? Will anyone interrupt to fetch equipment or make a phone call?

Will the writers be whisked off to physiotherapy during the workshop? If so, try and arrange the programme with the physios, so that the patients can have both their writing workshop and physiotherapy.

2. Will there be any helpers?

Make use of auxiliary nurses, visitors, carers, family to help scribe for those writers unable to write. It is good for these others to be involved. Otherwise you will have to scribe on your own. This can get complicated if you are the only person able to write in a large group. About four of five people is enough to make an interesting group.

(If possible do the exercise yourself and get the helpers to do it.) Make friends of the staff. Show them the work that has been produced. This helps to bring patient and carer closer and gives the occupational therapists a chance to see how their patients are progressing.

3. Introduce yourself and show the students any published work. Ask them to introduce themselves to the group and in a few words tell the group where they live, what family they have and what they do or did before they became ill. This helps everyone get out of 'patient' mode and revert to being people.

4. Take plenty of A4 paper and pens and pencils and find something for people to lean on for working if they are confined to a wheelchair.

5. Make sure the patients are comfortable. Make sure the writer's physical needs are met before and during the workshop. Does the writer want a drink? Should you call a nurse?

6. Take a box of tissues.

Poetry writing and especially reading it out loud brings out strong emotions. I find that the stroke rehabilitation workshop writers are particularly vulnerable. By all means sympathise and comfort but try and get them to carry on reading.

7. If you are going to be 'in residence' for any length of time, there should be a space you can call your own – a desk somewhere and a computer and printer to use, so you can go from workshop to desk to type the poems and print them out and give straight back to the writers. To see your poem in print, professionally reproduced is a great boost to one's confidence and sense of self worth. I endeavor to get workshop poems published in journals and magazines and encourage promising writers to continue their work alone. I give 'wardwork' to anyone who is keen to do more.

8. Enjoy the sessions. Relax and make them forget they are sick. Have some fun.

At the Hospice the workshops are almost always one to one. It is important to be aware of the patient's physical needs. If he has been given pain-killing drugs he might well be about to be rather sleepy. Work quickly to get the best out of the writing workshop. By all means chat first. You should be able to gauge what is important to the writer – his family, his wife, his work, his dog? Encourage him to write a poem about his wife or mother, his home or childhood. Use any of the following exercises to help. Even a very short piece will be valued by his loved ones.

III

The Exercises

EXERCISE 1

Subject: "This morning"
(The first Boundervean workshop)

Notes:
I talked them through it:

What did you see when you arrived?
Who did you meet?
Sounds, smells of Boundervean?
How did you feel?

The objective was to write for five minutes then read it out. Mary went early. Said "poetry was wimpy. Men who wrote poems were wimps." Gary, who is partially sighted, dictated to me and I scribed for him. Heather wrote about catching the bus that morning.

I suggested that they bring in a more finished piece about the morning next session. I showed how to do that, underlining the important words and changing any cliched phrases for more interesting ones.

I left each of them with a copy of several poems, just to prove that anyone can write a poem about anything:

'Love in a Bathtub' by Sujahata Bhatt;
'This is Just to Say' by William Carlos Williams;
'Celia, Celia' by Adrian Mitchell.

BUS
Eight minutes to catch the bus!
Haven't got the bus fare-
Natasha lends me 42p.
Seven minutes to catch the bus!
Forgotten my tobacco,
Go back in the house fumbling with keys.
Five minutes to catch the bus!
Can't find my tobacco.
Four minutes to catch the bus!
Go without my tobacco.
Four minutes to catch the bus!
The bus comes two minutes early.
Heather Ashworth, Boundervean

BROKEN DARK DAY
Broken dark day.
No room for cars,
indoor light parked-
acolytes, waiting.

Dog as a rug,
could just get in!
Sounds of belonging
to these I belong.

Notices galore, the well-trooped
hall; a coffee ordered,
contact made. Engage
the ashtray, that dark Tuesday.
Charles Goate, Boundervean

17

EXERCISE 2

Subject: 'When I hear your name'
Notes:
When I hear your name
I hear...
I see...
I smell...
I want...

Make first and third lines rhyme
Second and fourth lines rhyme
Write down words that rhyme or explore the use of half-rhymes.
e.g.-
Name -am, dam, ham, jam, lamb, sublime, dime, mime, time, home, I'm, come,
dome, foam, groom, broom, come, comb, womb, come, boom, coomb, doom, groom,
some, tomb.
Go through alphabet to find full rhymes -
e.g., aim, blame, came, dame, fame, game, lame, maim, same, tame,

PAUL
When I hear your name
I see the way you show your love
I hear your caring tender words
I feel the whisper of your touch.
When I hear your name
I think of the sea you love so much
I want to be with you forever.
Rosalyn Williams, St Julia's Hospice, Dec 24th 1996

WHEN I HEAR YOUR NAME
When I hear your name
I hear sweet birdsong
I see a lightning flame
I taste you on my tongue

18

I love you more that I can say
I want to eat you every day.
When I hear your name
I hear popgroups in my mind
I see a very well-matched game
even though I am half blind.
I want you to set my heart aflame.
Martin Coade, Marie-Therese, Hayle

WHEN I HEAR YOUR NAME
When I hear your name
I hear my home's love calling me back
I see the great sea's sparkling foam
I smell the salt tang of the waves as they break
I want to swell in your heart, to share its calm.

When I hear your name
I hear my own soul speak its need
I see a road that leads all ways, but never home
I smell the musty sadness of an autumn glade
I want to weave you onto my cold life's loom.
Darryl Gray, Student OT, Marie Therese, Hayle.

LIKOH - NORTH BORNEO GIRL
When I hear your name
I see the trees full of glow-worms
all on and off at the same time;
I feel the mud under my feet
when I returned to camp.
I taste salty water and remember
when I fell in the swamp.
I want the happiness we have
for another thirty years
without you kneeling to me
as you did the first time we met.
Leon Guyselman, Stroke Rehabilitation Unit, City Hospital, Truro

LANCELOT
When I hear your name
I hear Old Time dance music.
The first time we met
I wore high heels, a buttercup
yellow dress with full skirt.
I thought you were too tall.
You picked me up in the middle
of the dance floor,
stood me on your feet.
My long hair hung down my back.
You walked me home
put your arm around my waist.
You were my shining knight
Swept me off my feet.
Jeanette Thomas, Stroke Rehab Unit, City Hospital, Truro

BELOVED
When I hear your name
I see the moon the stars the sun
I feel the silence of the sky
I hear your soft voice all the time.
When I hear your name
I see your brightly twinkling eyes
and I want you.
Teresa Finnegan, St Julia's Hospice

HAMISH
When I hear your name
I see you jumping, tail wagging.
I feel your rough tongue licking my face -
I fight against it with no success.
I put on the lead and walk up the hill
over the style
slip the leash.
You take a quick look and off.
You never catch a rabbit except once.
They are always near the hedge.

When you are tired I whistle
and you return
and so home.
Chris Pearson, Rehab Unit, City Hospital, Truro.

EXERCISE 3

Subject: 'The Furniture Game'
Notes:
Think of someone you love or despise. Describe that person as if
he is -
A piece of furniture:
- an antique walnut bureau, marked and shiny with time.
- an old sofa, falling apart.
- a tallboy, holding many secrets.
- a whatnot with many shelves.
- a battered chair, one leg wobbly.
- a comfortable bed, broad, firm, safe.

A vehicle of some sort:
- a speeding sport's car, skidding around corners.
- a rickety bus, full of smoke upstairs and plump shoppers downstairs.
- a bicycle made for two.
- a liner, gleaming, a floating hotel.
- a bobbing sail boat.
- a child's scooter, discarded on the grass.

A sort of weather:
- stormy, with big skies and scudding clouds.
- sunny, warm, the air like cotton wool.
- a rain storm with angry hail hitting the glass.
- hurricane wind destroying all before it.

A type of landscape or place:
- a wood with bluebells in shady places.
- wide open prairie, with long grass swept by the wind.
- a little field with buttercups and daisies.

An animal:
- a lion hunting a kill
- a magpie, always after something new, chattering loudly.
- a robin taking bread crumbs from a hand.
- a warthog rolling in the mud.
- a sly snake slithering.
- a stallion, powerful, untamed.
- a pussy cat asleep by the fire.

An emotion:
- anger, happiness, pride, anxiety, guilt.

November 5, 1996 Marie Therese Unit, St. Michael's Hospital, Hayle Note: Martin Coade has MS and is in a wheelchair. He is a cheerful man in his early forties who is very disabled and cannot see. He drinks tea through a straw. I push his wheelchair into the pleasant room where I hold the weekly workshops. He lives with his eighty seven year old mother who looks after him with the assistance of several health carers. He needs a hoist to get in and out of bed. He has written verses before. He shows me his work. There are some strongly coloured abstract paintings with them. He did these before he lost his sight. He speaks slowly and with difficulty. I scribed for him.

The Furniture Game is a simple way of getting people to use metaphor when they write poetry. It opens writers' minds to new possibilities of expression.For Martin, it resulted in the following:

MOTHER
She is a fairly well-worn sofa, a little tattered
but my restful lifesaver.

She is a space-shuttle allowing me to make
discoveries, blasting off but landing soft.

She could be a train but probably not
because she is always on time.

She is sunshine that allows life and love to grow.
She is a soft valley with a gently stream flowing to the sea.

She is a lioness bringing food to me
- her cub.
She gives me love and I do love her too.

Note: A nurse assistant wrote this -
MY SON
He is a chest of drawers
with lots of drawers to investigate.
He is a comical old car
that often goes wrong
but can always be mended.

He is a sunny autumn day,lots of leaves swirling
like a whirlwind.
Moorland rocks and tors -
but edged by green valley.

A sometimes lost
young bear cub playful
but eventually dangerous.
He makes me fearful
and excited all in one go.
Cathy O'Callaghan, Marie Therese, Hayle

Workshop at St. Julia's Hospice, Hayle, 27 November, 1996
Note: I met Vic, in the day room, telly on, with another young
woman named Sue. Vic's Dad, Albert, was out shopping for him.
Vic was lying in a chair in his shorts and T-shirt. He was plugged
into various machines and needed more pain killing drugs as I
arrived. He was pretty drowsy with slurred speech all the time
and became very sleepy. I rolled a cigarette for him - Golden
Virginia - in Rizlas. I haven't done that for over thirty years but
at least it was smokeable. He smokes a lot through boredom, he
said. He couldn't use his right hand because he had a lot of pain

23

in his shoulder and couldn't lift it. His hand was swollen and the physio was due shortly. When his dad arrived Vic asked to have his legs covered with a blanket. His dad attended lovingly to his every need. He had brought in new jogging pants for him and chicken and beetroot, which he was going to prepare for him.

Albert did not want to write, just listen. After I had written down some history as Vic told it, I got him to write a poem based on the 'furniture game'. Sue tried to do it too, but got on very slowly by herself. She was leaving at the weekend but said if she finished it she would leave it for me.

Vic was increasingly sleepy and kept nearly burning himself with his cigarette. But he dictated and I wrote down his poem about his dad. He admitted it was very hard to talk as he got older, though he always had been good friends with his dad. Vic was pleased at the end when I read back what he had said about his dad; it was a poem that showed both his love and respect. They cried together.

First, I explained that I would ask questions and write down Vic's answers and make a poem from his words. Then I asked, 'What would your father be if he was a thing, an object?' After saying 'That's a bloody stupid question!' he went on to state, 'A brick.'

Q. 'What would he be if he was a vehicle?'
A. 'A Duran.'
Q. 'What's that?'
A. 'An American car, like a Rolls Royce, only better. It was THE car.'
Q. 'What sort of weather is he like?.'
A. 'Sunny and warm.'
Q. 'What sort of landscape do you think of when you think of your father?'
A. 'A golf course, somewhere warm.'
Q. 'If he was an animal what would he be?'
A. 'A stallion — a bit wild, untamed, free.'
'Last line — How does he make you feel?'
A. 'Safe!'

This is the resulting poem -

24

DAD
He's a brick,
he's like a Duran -
the American version of a Rolls Royce -
but better.
It was THE car.
He is sunny and warm,
he's a golf course
somewhere warm.
He's a stallion, a bit wild,
untamed, free,
but he makes me feel safe.
Victor Turner, St Julia's Hospice, Hayle.

Note: At the first Boundervean session I gave everyone a pen or
pencil and some A4 paper. To break the ice we did a group poem
as this group knew each other quite well. The group chose the
partially sighted, dapper young man, Gary, to write about. I asked
each person there to describe him as if he was a piece of furniture,
an animal, and a type of weather.Gary's poems are always printed
larger with the hope that he can see them.

GARY IS
GARY IS A COMFORTABLE CHAIR.
MOOSE LOOSE ABOUT THE HOUSE,
A POSH POOL TABLE.
HE'S A SUNNY DAY,
EVERY CLOUD HAS A SILVER LINING.
Heather Ashworth, Mary Phillips, Charles Goate, Shirley Lillie

Note: To get writers to make a poem about someone they love I
often use a simple exercise , a variation on the furniture game.
Think of the person as if she or he is a natural element, water -
river, stream, ocean; air, wind, weather, sky, a volcano, an
earthquake, a tornado, a whirlwind, anything that can be
developed as an idea, used as a devise to describe that person
and his personality and life.

JOYCE
Fresh clear water bubbling down a rocky bed,
persistently finding its way between the rocks
until its reaches its goal.
It can be deviated
but will not be stopped
until it reaches where it wants to go,
picking up leaves and twigs and carrying
them along between the obstructions
until they reach the end and into
the safe clear waters of the pond.
Roy Glanville, Rehab unit, City Hospital, Hayle

FOR DEREK
He is like a garden,
informal but organised
with wild flowers, shrubs and trees.
He is a wild rose,
a bit prickly now and again.
He is a bird, a falcon,
able to fly freely, high over
the hills of Zennor.
He is a sunny evening,
the sun going down over Zennor,
the rocky wildness,
the calm of the evening.
He makes me happy. There is a togetherness.
Ivy Clayden, St Julia's Hospice

Note: Saw Steve - Stanley Stephens who is hoping to get married
on Sunday, in Truro. I suggested he write a poem to his fiancee,
Lindsey.

FOR LINDSEY, FOUR DAYS BEFORE OUR WEDDING
Lindsey is a haven of peace,
a need that must be fulfilled,
partnership that balances,
comfort that is warm.
Trust that fulfils itself eternally.

The reminders that I have
are feeling at peace but perhaps
slightly mischievous.
Why are women always thought of as cats?
Because that feline element

has a touch of cruelty
can be wary in repose and in action
but always the love returns.
The pleasure is that love is always requited.
How lucky l am!
Steve Stephens, St Julia's Hospice, Hayle

Note: At the hospice one day I met Brian and his wife, Valerie.
He was dubious about writing but understood after I talked to him
for a bit. His wife said she did not know but maybe there were
things he wanted to say to her but could not and she left us alone.
He started to work on a poem for her but quickly became very
emotional and I apologised and went. I told his wife he obviously
loved her very much and she replied she was very lucky.

VALERIE
She is everything
a camellia, pink and white,
like our favourite flower,
she flowers in the bleak winter
Brian Stevens, St Julia's Hospice

EXERCISE 4

Subject: 'Love or Hate Poem' (variation of Furniture Game)
Notes: Write about someone you love or hate
Describe them as if they are -
A sort of weather - wild, frosty, slushy snow, drizzle, sunny and warm.
A colour - elaborate - blue as a jazz trumpeter, red as a matador's cloak.
A sound - banging drums, flapping wings, bell ringing, racing car.
A landscape - wild sea, calm river, dual carriageway, rolling hills, snow-capped mountain, deep silent valley.
A smell - warm bread, coffee roasting, baby's breath, cat's fur, honeysuckle, Old Spice, bath salts, wet dog, apple blossom.
An animal, bird or insect -
A plant - a single elm after the avenue has died of disease.
A sound -
An emotion.

Note: Met Gill Stillwell who has been at St Julia's for a week She used to be a teacher at one time and enjoyed the challenge of the poetry session, even sending her husband away when he arrived to visit her, saying she was enjoying herself and would he come back in ten minutes. I asked her to write about her three children as if they were landscapes. She wanted to read it to her husband when he returned to see if he recognised who it described, and he was a while returning so I started her on another poem about her husband, starting with the line - If I could, I would give you... Gill made a start before he returned, so I left it with her and asked her to complete it.

THREE CHILDREN

She is a field of poppies
With a granite and slate roofed cottage.
Cornflowers and daisies surround.
Velvety poppies visited by bees and butterflies,
A black cat stretches on the garden wall.

He is open spaces, sunny skies,
Lively sea, black headed gulls,
Billowing windsurfers,
Waves lapping, evening, sun sinking.

And the last child is dawn in a grassy paddock
With a white picket fence,
The grass succulent and green.
Morning star, mauve sky.
The last owl hoots, the first foal whinnies,
Mother replies.
Gill Stillwell, St Julia's Hospice

STEPHEN
Sometimes he is like calm water that small children paddle in
And other times he is like a high tide at Pendennis Point
With the waves crashing in.

MICHAEL
He is like a sunny beach with golden sands,
A cool breeze in the background.

TONY
Tony is like one of those small secretive coves by the Lizard
That you discover on a magical mystery tour,
And that you didn't know was there.

PETER
He is like the treacherous coast of Cornwall
With sharp, devious, hidden rocks,
That the coastguard would warn you to steer clear of
Elizabeth Parry, St Julia's Hospice.

29

EXERCISE 5

Subject: 'Childhood Memory'
Notes: Perhaps we only remember the awful things- accidents, hurt, never the pleasant times.
Nevertheless I do recall the feeling of having my blanket tucked around me in the pram. The safe feeling. The church at Patrington where I was christened - like a cathedral with stained glass.
Early memory or even the first thing you remember?
Or just the atmosphere of childhood e.g. - warmth, hot chocolate, reading in bed, cuddling with parents, playing after school. Walking home alone, traffic-free streets.
Toys - favourite teddy, dolls, Dinky cars.
Write down anything that comes to mind about the memory. Do you remember any
Details about the weather - storm, sunny.
Where were you? In a house, bus, garden, street, meadow?
Who was with you? What happened? Tell it as a story first. Tell the group if you
want. Or just write notes and read them out. Then we find the best words or most important elements and go from there.
*Marie Therese House, 20 August 1996*Note: Barbara had worked hard on her piece after starting the first draft last week. She had lots more detail and the picture of the visit to the fish market was vivid. We worked on it - cutting out the prose and turned it into more of a poem shape.

MOTORBIKE RIDE TO BILLINGSGATE MARKET ON HER FIFTH BIRTHDAY
Small arms gripped, hugged the solid body of the man.
She tucked her head into his warm back.
Wind tugged the scarf tied around her head.
Their voices rose in song lost on engine roar.

A soft dawn broke the sky as they stepped
onto dew-damp stones, became part of the buzz.
Odour of sea surrounded, invaded,
contained the child, blue eyes wide.

Mountains of mussels, glistening black.
Her fingers dug into cold damp shells.
She shook with excitement, eyes full of pink -
vibrant pink. Sharp, crisp prawns rained.
She held out hands to catch glistening, glowing jewels.
Soft brown shrimps and red scooped into gallon measures.
Voices in bid, barter and laughter rose and fell.
A hand pressed her shoulder - time to go -
fish and sea smells clung to her
as the scene receded through grown-ups' legs.
Barbara Faragher, Marie Therese Unit, Hayle

THE PHOTOGRAPH
Fairways on sunny days
I remember the dog always
ran after cars in the lane;
how we played cowboys and Indians
in the rain.
I was always an Indian.
How I went exploring in the
jungle back garden and fell down a pit -
A bit smelly and wet,
I was afraid of it after that.

But here we are holding hands,
My twin sister and I,
in our pretty ballet dresses
white innocence and naivity
shining from our eyes.
Tresses neatly tied into
bows - mine scarlet like a rose -
Jo's pale blue - echoing
our unfolding natures,
She fair and plump and slow
and I dark and skinny and
longing to take flight.
Juliana Geer - Auxiliary - Marie Therese Unit, Hayle

BOY SCOUTING, a series
by Graham Gratton

COUNTRYSIDE BADGE
Good manners to wildlife,
flora and fauna,
closing farm gates,
following the country code.
Knowing names.
Shrews, badgers, foxes, otters,
water rats are water voles.
Dandelions, foxgloves, bluebells,
buttercups and daisies.

FIRE-LIGHTING BADGE
I remember another warm day,
a small pile of dry and dead grass
gathered with bracken,
then small twigs, then bigger twigs,
then larger firewood.
Sun on broken glass made the fire
smoulder, then I blew on it to make a flame.
A platform of wood for the dixie.
What joy, later, to sew on the fire-lighting badge
on my scout shirt.
Sewing was another scouting skill.

WOOD-CUTTING BADGE
I collected dead wood - birch, oak, beech,
broad-leaf deciduous
hardwood from Gorton Wood
chopped with a hand-axe
nice and sharp.

MAINTENANCE OF THE AXES - HAND AXE AND FELLING AXE

Cheek of the blade,
oiling the cheeks to keep away the rust,
sharpening on Carborundum
or ironstone.
Linseed oil stroked into the heft.
If you took your time
it made the axe handle supple.
Less danger of fracture.

I was the cat's whiskers
in my badge encrusted shirt
which I had washed and ironed to earn
another badge and another whisker.

CHILDHOOD

Born opposite each other in Cherry Garden Street in Mousehole.
She's four months older than me.
Used to play in the harbour with boats.
The girls cleaned the rocks with a piece of brick.
Used to boil limpets there or eat them raw.
Caught shrimps in nets made out of mother's curtains.
Sewn onto wire ring with a bamboo stick.
I was in the water more than anything, swimming, boating.
Had my own boat, about twelve foot clinker built.
Could rig a sail if I wanted. I was ten.
Fished from the boat with a light line,
caught turbot, megrim, cut off the poisonous spine,
gar, bass - my best bass was eleven pounds.
Donald Nancarrow, St Julia's Hospice, Hayle

EXERCISE 6

Subject: 'Open the door'
Notes: This exercise was sparked by Miroslav Holub's poem 'The Door', taken from *Lifelines* 2. All I suggest for this exercise is that writers start with the line -"Go and open the door."

THE DOOR

Go and open the door.
    Maybe outside there's
    a tree, or a wood,
    a garden,
    or a magic city.

Go and open the door,
  Maybe a dog's rummaging.
  Maybe you'll see a face,
or an eye,
or a picture
         of a picture.

Go and open the door,
  If there's a fog
  it will clear.

Go and open the door.
  Even if there's only
  the darkness ticking,
  even if there's only
  the hollow wind,
  even if
nothing
  is there,
go and open the door.

At least
there'll be
a draught.
Miroslav Holub (b1923) Translated by Ian Milner

GO AND OPEN THE DOOR
Go and open the door.
Maybe I will find
A hairbrush that I can hold,
A pen that I can write with.
Maybe I will find a flexibility
That I never had before
In fingers I can use to touch someone's hand,
To wash my face,
To brush my teeth,
To stroke my dog.
Maybe I could use a computer.

Go and open the door.
Maybe I will find a car that I can drive.
I could go anywhere.
Kerry Jackson, Marie Therese House

THE DOOR
When I was a little girl,
I always wanted to see the other
part of the world, but how?
In my dreams I'm always wishing and hoping
that someone will open the door for me.

I know there is a lot to see out there -
Please can someone open the door?

I'm suffocated, I need fresh air,
nearly blind - I need to see the light
and glance the blue sky.
I want to leave now,
please unlock and open the door.
Mel Lasbury, Nursing Assistant, Rehab Unit, City Hospital, Truro

35

GO AND OPEN THE DOOR
Life is full of doors.
All have to be opened.
Loads of surprises lie in wait
sometimes wonderful
some the stuff of nightmares.
All must be gone through.
There's no peeping through the keyhole.
Treasures are for some, tragedies for others.
Life lies in wait.
Days of brilliant sunshine,
oceans of turquoise furnished with
delicate corals inhabited with brilliant bejewelled fish,
fluorescent squid, fierce barracuda, molluscs
and lumbering lobsters.

Go and open the door.
The ocean of turquoise has become a boiling cauldron
with prancing white horses cresting the waves.
Gone are the jewels of the deep, cowering in corners and crevices.
Wind and lashing rain have swept the sun away.
Dorothy Biddick, Rehab Unit, City Hospital, Truro

GO AND OPEN THE DOOR
The world is full of maybe's
Push hard, there's a chink of light
Life is there where you left it
Push hard, go for it.

Go and open the door
To a living carpet of blue
Sunlight filtering through breeze-filled trees
Hazy mist rising from nodding bells.

Take breath, pull in the scented air
Fill the lungs, push the door.
Open to a castle top
To absail down to breathless crowds.
The air is warm, full of excitement and fear.
Barbara Faragher, Marie Therese House, Hayle

I CAN SEE THEM PLAYING THERE
My husband opens the door for me because I can't.
The handles are too high to see what is out there.
The hedge was full of lilac
the scent was lovely.
In the winter they were bare.
Behind the garden was a road
and then there were fields
and cows were in the fields.
We used to go across the fields to go shop
or get some water for our mum.
We used to play in the field with my brothers and sisters.
I can see them playing there.
Jeanette Thomas. Rehab unit, City Hospital, Truro

EXERCISE 7

Subject: 'Being in Hospital'
Notes: I have used this exercise with most of the patient groups I
work with, adapting the questions to their situation.
Did you sleep well or badly?
Did you dream? What?
What did you eat for breakfast?
What is the name of the nurse?
What is the name of the occupational therapist?
Is the sun shining? Is it raining?
Did you talk to anyone?
What happened?
Any exercises?
Can you walk?
Can you lift your arm?
Can you talk?
Can you eat and drink by yourself?
Can you read? Can you write?
How do you feel?
These questions like others in the exercises are triggers to memory
or thought, helping the writer get started. As soon as you write
something it is easy to carry on writing.

HOSPITAL MORNING
Breakfast starts with grapefruit and toast
and pleasant smiles from the lovely nurses.
A bowl of water is brought in for a wash
which makes you feel so much better
and after a shave and clean of teeth
you begin to feel human once more.
Peter Kemp, Rehab Unit, City Hospital

38

ROY GLANVILLE ASKS
Why am I in hospital?
I feel well, it is just that my body
does not respond to my wishes.
My arm, hand and leg feel strange
and will not perform the simple functions
that they have carried out for years.
My brain tells them what I want
but they are incapable of carrying out
the instructions passed on.
Simple movement functions like
moving in a certain way to pick up an article or to move
to hold something which is on the table next to me.

What is going to happen to me?
What does the future hold?
Will I wake up, is this all a dream?
No, nurses and doctors assure me, you are
recovering from a stroke.
It will take time - much time.

How did it happen?
Why did it happen?
What does the future hold?
what future?
Roy Glanville, Rehab Unit, City Hospital, Truro

EXERCISE 8

Subject: 'Schooldays'
Notes: Think about Junior School or secondary school, boarding, private, prep school, convent school; Sunday School. School teachers; head teacher; school friends; games; best at which subject? Dinner; packed lunch; milk; sweet shop; playground games - marbles, skipping, cricket teacher reading a story. Bullying, best friend, school trip, treat. Sunday school outing, stealing. unhappiness, enjoyment, memories of incidents - accidents, teacher dying, friend leaving, lying, cheating, exams, uniform, lavatories; dinner ladies, school caretaker, cat, pond, garden. Getting the cane! Remember sounds - children shouting, laughing, footsteps in corridors, stairs, singing, piano, music, songs in games, dinner plates. Whistle blowing, bell ringing. Smells - dinner, sponge pudding and treacle, minced meat; stubby little bottles of warm milk on radiator, children's feet. Sweat of changing rooms, chalk. Teacher's face powder.

Sights - paintings; nuns' long habits and white tall head-dresses.

Events - ear ache in playground - abcess bursting. Refusing to eat minced meat, sat crying over cold food, gagging on it. Best at spelling. Book prizes -Poetry book. Packed lunch. Cold toast and bread and butter pudding. Freezing as I got dressed icicles inside window.Cycling to school. Walking to school, taking off all my clothes on way home.

Write down all you can remember. Put each thought on separate line. Then go through choosing important or interesting words. Weed out unnecessary or cliched thoughts - Underline important words, then rewrite using only underlined words, putting each thought or phrase on separate line so it begins to look like a poem.

As an example, I sometimes read one of my own poems:

40

OXO
I stole
A hot penny burning holes.
Guilt blazed me
Ready for Hell.

I craved
Beefy black brown stuff,
Sweet harshness
Fired my mouth.

I saved
A sweating morsel
Placed in bright foil,
Deviant taste.

We moved.
Was my sin known?
Banished, punished -
At my new school my halo shone.
Ann Kelley

SUNDAY SCHOOL LIE
'Have you a pet?'
I didn't count Tiddles
who was older than me,
more like an uncle
who kept out of my way

'A pony'
They believed me,
unbelievably
and I had to elaborate
inventing gymkanas, rosettes.

God seeped in hymns
to my tottering soul
so I killed off my pet
with a tragic cough.

But on the annual treat
to London zoo
cold winds blew
fatal words -
'Sad about Ann's pony!'

'What pony?' Mother said.
Thrashed in front of all
I noted through icy tears
cool elegant curves
of the penguin pool.
Ann Kelley

SCHOOLDAYS
Navy gym slip, white blouse, white socks black shoes.
If it was dry we walked, if wet, I rode on the bus
with my brothers and sisters and friends.

Play - I used to do the crab - crab crawl -
you used to go on all fours backwards,
lie down on the ground,
push yourself up and start walking.

Netball, rounders, hula hoop.
Mr Scott we called Mr Scotty Pop-
He chased us and we used to run away.

We used to make our own fun
like hopscotch, Kick the Can.

Up the Burrows - the old tin mines
where old bikes were thrown away
used to make up bikes with no brakes and no tyres
and ride down the hills.
Push the bike back up and ride it down again.

Three of us in a bungalow bath - a galvanised tub,
we took it off mother's wall and used it as a slide.
Til we got a hole in it and we hung it back up.

Old prams - used to make a dandy, a go-cart -
and ride down the hill.
Jeanette Thomas, Stroke Rehab Unit, City Hospital, Truro

SCHOOLDAYS
Skipping - In comes Jack
Cricket - I shut my eyes.
My brother Michael said 'You're out!'
I said I was not.
He said 'You are,' and he left me in.

There were four sisters. There was me and Mary, Elizabeth and
Veva.
and Michael, Trevor, Paul, Nigel, John, Maxwell and Malcolm.

Summer
We used to walk to Porthreath and Porthtowan
and swim in the sea and in the pool.
Aunty Ruth and her sixteen children - can't remember their
names -
people used to say - here comes the North Country clan.
Tonkins used to come up and play cricket on the beach with us -
Edna, Brian, Ann, Michael, Raymond, can't remember the
others.
Used to walk to school with them.
Used to have ice blocks, in little cubes, different colours.
Used to look forward to that.

Winter
In snow - used to have soup.
Sit around the stove in a circle
with our coats on to keep warm
One day we all fell into a snow drift in the hedge -
all my brothers and sisters and myself. Eleven of us.
My eldest brother, Michael, pulled us out.
Played netball.
Wasn't very good at that.
Wasn't tall enough.
Jeanette Thomas, Stroke Rehab Unit, City Hospital, Truro

THUMBS UP
Thumbs up - swinging
Thumbs down - dodgy.

Miss Goble we called Gobbleguts.
Nature walks, acorns, flowers.

My friend Tina we called Weeny.
I was no good at rounders.

Shrimping in the holidays
cycling the lanes to school,
dodge ball.

The poor caretaker,
they teased him, were rude to him
but I was not.
Shirley Lillie, Boundervean

RUGBY
Mr Vingo - 'Why can't I ever score a try?'
I replied - 'You're on the wrong side.'
Got mud all over me, I scored tries.
Gary Gibson, Boundervean

EXERCISE 9

Subject: 'When I get old'.
Note: Read 'Warning' by Jenny Joseph. Start with line 'When I
am old...'

WHEN I GET OLD
When I get old I will be
A shrivelled up prune.
I will wear jeans and I'll bomb
Man-U football ground.
I will fly a Spitfire.
I will go down to the sea,
It *will be clean.*
Mary Phillips, Boundervean

WHEN I GET OLD
When I get old
I'll not be told
to 'Turn that music down,'
but take my ghetto blaster
...and get plastered
in every pub in town.
I'll rinse my hair
with purposeful care
in shocking purple dye
and moan for fun
and spit at some
rude children passing by.
Whilst wearing 'Sunday best'
I'll do the SAS...
and absail from tall buildings.
I'll roll in blindly drunk
and kick up a blue funk -
when the dentist does my fillings.
I won't be an old trout
and you'll find me chilling out with all the young dudes!
Jenny Rowe, Prince's Trust, Marie Therese House, Hayle

EXERCISE 10

Subject: 'Lost and Found'
Notes: Name six things you have lost in your life - innocence, a pet, a friend, member of family, ability to walk, to write, to draw, play the piano, dance, temper, a race, a bet, a wager, freedom.

Name six things you have found in your life - happiness, contentment, a family, a home, friends, money, treasure, peace of mind, a toy, gloves, a purse, a skill.

Often the writer will go off on a limb and write about something else entirely. Great! These exercises are only a tool to help with the writing process - a stick to beat the donkey with to make it move - a trigger to the memory and mind. There are no rules and regulations about poetry - nothing we can't ignore, anyway. The important thing is to write the truth: it is always worth reading.

LOST
I've been searching for my companions
down in empty crystal canyons,
the aimless blade of science
slashed the pearly gates.
An eagle flies descending
around rivers bending, my transient nodes of thought
seem to have faded away.
Charlie Shone, Stroke Rehab Unit, City Hospital, Truro

RECURRING DREAM
I am with a small boy - you.
I show you my childhood -
beach, funfair, quiet streets, sun.
Then you are not there.
I search for you.
Heaped dirty snow
on the darkening estuary beach
and the tide flooding fast.
Ann Kelley

LOST
I lost my purse - stolen, and lost seeing justice done.

I lost my springer spaniel, Pippa - stroking her golden coat,
hearing her play with the children,
the fun and laughter this brought from them.

When I was six I slipped and lost the school race.
I got up and ran on but only came second,
so we didn't get the cup.

I lost my temper with the children.

I have lost the fun of shopping.
Running up the stairs of Dorothy Perkins
choosing and changing clothes on my own
then the hurrying and scurrying through
the bright happy Christmas streets,
home to my promised deep deep bubbly, scented bath,
a long soak, my own privacy,
no need of help or assistance
on into the bedroom to my new dress and dancing shoes
and to my waiting husband,
tripping around the dance floor in his arms.

Being able to walk on a sandy beach
paddling in a hot August.

I have lost taking for granted what I used
to take for granted.
I have lost wasting away hours.
Carol Heardson, Marie Therese House, Hayle, January 7, 1997

LOST

Lost my healthy appetite
and found an elephant's.
I feel at every meal
I pack my trunk.
It works overtime
swinging to and fro
like a demented pendulum.

Eating fills one
of time's empty pockets,
moving the slow wheel of time
turning the world
with well oiled sprockets.
Dorothy Biddick, Stroke Rehab Unit, City Hospital, Truro

THE BUTTON

He was ill.
My brothers and sisters
took turn to care for him.
I was on dialysis
so could not help him.

When he died
my father had a button
missing from his shirt
so I gave him one of mine.
Jeanette Thomas, Stroke Rehab Unit, City Hospital, Truro

Note: Give your poem a good title.Perhaps the first line or another good line. Perhaps the name of the person it is about. A title can add to the message you are trying to communicate. A good title is an important part of the poem.

One day at Boundervean there was only Diana from the group. I set the poem - LOST and she wrote movingly about her baby who had to be adopted when he was two and she was in a psychiatric hospital.

GARY
I gave birth to you, son
I was young
and not so strong
you cried and cried.

I was sick of mind
hadn't seen you for some time,
when I gave you away
you called me 'lady' waved 'bye bye.'

I imagine you blond and tall
your eyes blue and clear
I see you in my dreams
only you could have that smile.
Diana Humphrey-Snow

Note: She produced another poem about this traumatic period of her life.

CHILD ALONE IN A BUGGY
You sat alone by the gate.
she couldn't wait.
Locked doors and empty house.
Why did I bring you here?

Your smiling face
your sparkling eyes
looked happy to see me.

The danger that awaited you
before I came!
Where do I put the blame?
Diana Humphrey-Snow

FOUND
I found living alone wonderful.
I found the cat,
Found three good friends,
peace from God
I found the lovely gardens,
birds singing, lovely.
At Boundervean I found
I loved weaving and sewing.
Shirley Lillie, Boundervean

LOST
Lost
All my possessions.
Freedom
All left behind.
Found
A bright blue sky
And a summer's day
In Cornwall
I have nothing
But a bag of clothes
And a broken radio
But I am happy here.
Heather Ashworth, Boundervean

LOST
My pet dog Pepper who looked after the tools
and guarded them from thieves;
my cousin Stephen - we ran along the sand,
his blond hair and smile.
My feeling of being nervous.

I have lost this Christmas
and the bloom of last Summer,
the river with its clear water,
herons balancing on one leg.
Ros Williams St Julia's Hospice, January 7th, 1997

EXERCISE 11

Subject 'Family members' or A Memory of someone important to you like a pet.'

Notes: This section is larger than most, and can be broken down into separate exercises for separate workshops. However, since all of the topics are variations on the same theme, they are grouped together.

First line - Start of by imagining the person you have chosen to write about in a room or shed or garden or work-place suitable to them.

Perhaps a mother knitting in a favourite armchair or cooking a stew; dressing in her finery for a dance.

Father hammering in a shed; harvesting potatoes from a vegetable patch; feeding his pigeons.

Next line or lines - Describe the place- the kitchenette floor was red, walls green,

cracked, chipped dishes on shelves; a pink flowered wallpaper; a large double bed;

cobwebs and dust layered the shelves;

Next - A smell, sounds, roast meat cooking; furniture polish; oil paint and turpentine;

scraping of chairs; dog barking.

Next - introduce your person or pet - she sucks her breath, stirs the pot.

Last line - what happens? - the cat purrs, or father snores, mother shouts.

FATHER
Write about a particular event you remember from childhood that involves your father.

CHIN PIE
'Do you want some chin pie?' asked Dad
What's chin pie? I asked, puzzled.
It was nine o'clock on a Saturday morning.
My Dad sat in the easy chair,

shirt sleeves rolled up.
He had not yet had a shave.
Mum was in the kitchen.

'Come up here and I'll show you.' Dad said.
I clambered up onto his knee.
He rubbed his face against mine, laughing.
It felt prickly like sand paper
Ow! Don't! Stop it!' I shrieked, giggling.
'What's the matter?
Don't you like chin pie?'
'No! It hurts! Geddoff!'
Heather Ashworth, Boundervean

TO DAD
Greedy pain our womb.
The peach is stone
the flesh is bone;
the part of us is brave
and it alone can save-.

I suppose there is a conflict,
that this must be written.
To begin hurt is not to end
surely
and you will look for an answer,
the void to trace.

It is answer enough
but not enough.
The migration of the eagle
will not carry but be there.

Soaring with a flock
he is there.
Shall I in the void?
In reproach perhaps,
security too it known.

I cannot fly but must
and want to

My friend indeed,
pinions and eye
not far if far .
Not there these days
It does not matter.
We'll soar time on from fear
the gristle human ligaments
the point always love.
Charles Goate, Boundervean

MOTHER
Write about your mother at any time you remember her best.
What was your favourite thing she cooked?
Did she wear pretty clothes?
What did she look like?
Was she attractive?
Her favourite phrase?
Her favourite child?
Did she dance?
What was she good at?
Did she like reading, gardening, bee-keeping, sewing, paying the piano, walking,
gossiping, listening to the radio - what? Mrs Dales Diary? The Archers?
Was she a good mother?
Did you like her?
Did she show you affection?
Describe her as best you can.

CLOTTED CREAM
Sunday morning
my mother made clotted cream.
Milk from the farm.
In the kitchen a big Belfast sink,
and a wooden draining board stood up after use.

Mother always had her pinny on and thick
furry lilac slippers.
A big woman - small but fat.

She'd have a big enamel pan of milk on the gas stove
warming slowly until a crust formed on top.
She skimmed it every time it formed
until no more formed.
We drank the leftover milk.
The clotted cream went into a big white cloam bowl.
Tea was splits with honey and cream
or banana and cream sandwiches -
mashed banana on one slice of bread,
an inch thick clotted cream on the other slice,
slapped together.
Malcolm Wilton, Marie Therese House

REMEMBER A GRANDPARENT:
Title could be the name you used - Nana, Gran, Pop,
Grandmother, Granny, Grandpop or their proper name.
First line- describe the house or place - room, shed, garden,
kitchen. What do you see? Heavy furniture, patterned rugs, fire
burning, pictures of flowers, jamjars of wild flowers, cup of tea
leaves, newspapers.
Next line - describe the smell of the place - cooking, flowers, dead
fish, mice, boot polish, overcooked greens.
Next - sounds - smashing of plates, shouting, whining dog, car
fight, kettle boiling, typewriter tapping, shoe polishing, piano
playing.
Next line - the grandparent is there - what is he or she doing?
Describe the action.
Something specific. What does he wear, look like, hair, eyes?
He looks up and says-?

FIRST MEMORIES
First memories are of my grandfather in his shed
making the model furniture
his hands gently carving the little pieces.

The hens in their shed jealously guarding their eggs.
Their beady eyes when I went to fetch the eggs.
The old cockerel runs like fury to get
to the hens past Grandfather's shed.

The cat on first meeting - Grandfather's cat,
spoilt and teased - bit me.
I was warned he would.

The lovely doll's house Grandfather made me.
I still have it.
It was made the same as the house we lived in.
Shirley Lillie, Boundervean

GRANDFATHER
The bungalow in Penzance -
dark brown patterned carpet,
gardening books, pictures
 and paintings of old Penzance.
Old county cricket balls on the mantel
and black and white striped
Everton Mints on the armchair.

The voice of David Gower,
the smell of stew, carrots, sprouts.
Grandad's old glasses propped up by his big nose,
his navy blue shirt with a paint-stained
hanky in the top pocket.

Muttering about umpires' decisions.
'How's things? Doing all right at school?
Spurs aren't doing well.'
James Lloyd Stewart. work experience student, Marie Therese House

IN MARY'S HOUSE
She is there -
The overstuffed room
the mantelpiece with its high Victorian vases
the mantle cloth with dusty tassels
icons of Mary whose calm smile seemed so out of place.

The other Mary, Nana,
small but hugely round
with arms and hands like a navvy's,
broad capable hands
hands that moved as she spoke
quickly and clearly like her big brown eyes,
white fire flashed from gold rings
that danced in the fire's light.
The smell of damp burning coal
mixed with the many human bodies
now compressed in the room,
laughter loud and long.
One of the many started to sing
soon the whole was alive with sound.
Voices sang, piano played, Nana clapped.

Then it would begin -
women sent to the kitchen to make thick sandwiches,
boys sent to the pub for crates of beer,
singing, drinking, talking, laughter
far into the night until the younger children fell asleep.
Barbara Faragher, Marie Therese House, Hayle

EXERCISE 12

Subject: Poem based on William Carlos Williams' 'Red Wheel Barrow' or 'This is Just to Say'

THIS IS JUST TO SAY -after William Carlos Williams
I have eaten
 the fruit of life
now I hope
to reach a higher plain
with the invisible
taste of truth.

As the doors
open in my mind
I want to be kind.
Sometimes the corridors
are full of bitter fruit.

I have eaten
now my path is clear
and I do dare
I have eaten all. *Diana Humphrey-Snow, Boundervean*

YOU CAN'T JUST SAY THAT (after William Carlos Williams)
I have eaten
The bike ride
Around the block

For some
Fresh sun air
Seeing
A girl.

Forgive me or her
In a window
So lush
Looking for custom. *Charles Goate*

THE BOTTOM RIGHT HAND CORNER (after William Carlos Williams)
So much depends
upon

The bottom right
digit

On the pale
keyboard

Why? Why? Why?
Charles Goate, Boundervean

Note: It is a useful trick to use the first lines of a well-known poem. It gets the poem going with a swing, gives it a professional rhythm, and challenges the imagination.

EXERCISE 13

Subject: 'Diary Poem'
Notes: This exercise is perhaps best set as homework. My suggestion to every writer is to keep a diary of what happened to them each day.

I ask them to write down something for each day of the week, even if it is only the way you feel, or that you did nothing but eat alone, stayed in, watched tv - then review and select one day to write about.

Mary, who uses a walking frame to move around, had been looking for a new place to live.

MONDAY
New house
rotten doors
steps - bad news.
Lovely window
no cupboards
smells, cold
can't use the bath
loo's old.
Mary Phillips, Boundervean

TUESDAY
A good day
Then on the way home
my head suddenly droops,
lops like a rag doll's.
At home Jenny uses the hoist
to lift me onto the bed.
I undress
then my arms fail to raise me.
She calls Gordon from the garden.
He moves me.
Martin Coade, Marie Therese House

MY FIRST STEPS
Monday - I did not do well
Tuesday - Today I walk up four steps
and down the corridor
up the main ward
and back to the four bedder.
 I think I done very well.
Jeanette Thomas, Rehab Unit, City Hospital, Truro

EXERCISE 14

Subject: 'The Night Before...'
Note: A joint poem. Take turns to make up a line, concerning
something which occurred the night before, and speak it out loud,
then the next person follows and so on. Be as inventive as you
like. Use dreams, events, thoughts, real or imagined moments.

CAT ON MY FEET
The unicorn square took my mind
and the cat needed food
(No crunching or mouse skull tonight).
All I do is sew
I am so full of woe,
I would sleep if I could
The unicorn bull was signed
I need a home
it could be made of wood
The room is too harsh with the moon
and the starlit sea is too bright...
Charles Goate, Mary Phillips and Ann Kelley - Boundervean.

EXERCISE 15

Subject: Haiku
Notes: Write a haiku - a poem of three lines of five, seven and five
syllables but don't worry too much about the syllables if it proves
too difficult.

Getting everything
in seventeen syllables
Is very diffic
(John Cooper Clarke)

Note: Charles wrote lots - here are a few:

The beach chatters
Free at peace, balmy after
Time left until dusk.

A little sliver
fillet pure of wine water
will right sanely save.

Laughter masked black
both joy sad and cry happy
mask base of life, dough.

Swam the blue ocean
fishy caught on lishy,
blue wide sapping blue.
Charles Goate, Boundervean

Note: The writers in the group read out the completed work from
last time. Then we discussed where changes could be made and
I offered to take the work home and print them. I do this every
time. The finished poem looks more professional when it is
printed. Often the handwriting is difficult to read and spelling is
wrong. I ask permission to correct the mistakes, and suggest
changing line endings where I think the poem would benefit.

EXERCISE 16

Subject: 'I remember'
Notes: A poem about place, childhood, an event, a regular
happening.
Read - 'I Remember, I Remember' by Thomas Hood; 'Adlestrop'
by Edward Thomas; 'Snake' by DH Lawrence; 'Blackberry
Picking' by Seamus Heaney - from *The Nation'sFavourite Poems*.

Paula wrote about tea treat, a Cornish traditional Sunday
School event, and Barbara wrote about guide camp. She was

61

amused when I pointed out her half rhymes in the last poem she
wrote. "Quite unintentional" she said.

I REMEMBER CAMP

I remember camp.
The wet field the lines of drunken tents
guy ropes slack, hanging with beads of dew
water dripping onto the neck as you ducked your head
to make your way out of the dark into the rising damp of a hot
new morning.
Oh! What a tantalising smell
wood smoke, pine resin oozing out of burning branches
blackened sausages, bacon sizzling, beans frying,
the hunger, both for food and a new day.
Oh! For the hunger of youth
the eagerness for life.
Evening the fire high
girls cross-legged in a large ring
tasted marsh mallows passed hand by hand,
old old songs.
Darkness with the rich smell and taste of hot chocolate ended the
day.
I remember camp.
Barbara Faragher, Marie Therese House, Hayle

MIXED UP WITH SQUIRREL

'Mum,' I said,
'What's a quarrel?'
Somehow I had got it mixed up with squirrel.
Mum was busy talking to another lady,
We were on our way to school
Through the churchyard.
I tugged at her hand.
'Mum,' I said, 'What's a quarrel?'
Heather Ashworth, Boundervean

A BORN ACTRESS
Our dressing table had three mirrors,
three images of me, the Andrew Sisters.

I dreamed of being famous on screen.
'Don't sit under the apple tree with anyone else but me.'

'Oh! Johnny' Oh! Johnny, how you can love!'
'He's the boogie woogie trumpeter from company B.'

My Joyce, my sister, teased me unmercifully,
even my mother, bless her, laughed at me.

She said I was a born actress, not like Joyce.
She was an open book, still is.
Pat Clarke, Rehab Unit, City Hospital, Truro

Note:The poems are often written and finished in one two hour
session. I often do not know if I will see the writer again so I try
and get them to produce something straight off. It gives them a
feeling of achievement and makes them feel they have something
worthwhile to give back, at a time when maybe they are unable
to help themselves physically and depend on nurses and carers
to move them, wash them, feed them and do all the basic things
they used to take for granted.

If I know the writer is going to be a patient in that ward for a
while, I offer them the chance of doing some 'homework' or
'wardwork'! They often enjoy the opportunity to write more once
they have got started. It relieves the boredom of life on the ward,
where often the only stimulation is the speech therapy session or
physiotherapy session each day. Some patients are lucky enough
to get occupational therapy but there is never enough of this The
writing encourages the stroke patients to use their hands and
memories. Maybe it even aids recovery.

TEA TREAT
I remember tea treat
I remember Sunday School.

I remember - used to have the name,
used to say who we were from
on a banner.

I walked to the Island,
my hair in a pony-tail,
walked with Julie along
on the path
just coming off Porthmeor Beach,
up the steps.
The washing laid out on the grass,
sheets of Downalong,
the women laying it on the Island.

We ate ham sandwiches,
plain current buns, no butter,
we drank pop.
We played games.
Use to go in the sea in our swimsuits.
A few people used to bring radios.

Church bands played
we sang hymns.
On the beach used to be a person
used to call out our names
for a gift before we went home.
I got a hymn book, blue.
Paula Fowler, Marie Therese House

EXERCISE 17

Subject: 'We met'
Notes:
WE MET
The place
The time -
The event - party, dance, pub, dinner party, school, college, shop.
His voice

His hair
His mouth
His stance
His words
His ears
His figure
His scent
His skin
His hands
His beard
His chest
His laugh
His eyes
Where we met
The song
Music
What did he say?
What happened next?

Note: Paula did all her own writing. The following is her draft:

TONY
We met.
Alone we went for a walk
alone.
We went to the beach
he had nice green eyes
quite a nice face   he was tall
his hair was nice quite long
his face said everything.

Note: The following finished piece has my suggested changes and
Paula's additions:

TONY
We met
alone,
we went for a walk.
Alone,
we went to the beach.
He had green
eyes
a kind round face.
He was tall
his hair was brown and long,
his face said
everything.
Paula Fowler, Marie Therese House

WE MET
We met at a dance.
I noticed her legs,
the gentleness of her voice,
high heels, short dress,
her long legs.

Her hair flowed freely, I do remember,
honey blonde.
Her eyes, pale blue, long dark lashes,
spoke words of love.
She was warm and glowing,

Hazel was her name.
We danced close.
Gary Weaver, Marie Therese House

EXERCISE 18

Subject: 'A romantic interlude'
Notes: A love poem about a particular occasion
Where? A dance floor; a party, by the sea; at school; at a friend's
house?
Remember the dress, the scent, her hair, his voice, her breath,
her lips; her legs, his
hands, his muscles.
Music - Jazz, classical, popular, piano, violins, a singer, a song, a
big band.
Sounds - her dress, taffeta, silk rustling, hush of muslin, stiff cloth,
denim, harshness on skin. Rattling windows, waves crashing.
Tastes - onions, oysters. treacle tart, lemon, sour, salt tears,
tobacco, whiskey.
Smells - flowers, drink,
Touch - silk, harsh, strong arms, delicate, passionate, possessive.
Feeling of joy, passion, strength, fear, awkwardness.

CORNISH GIRL AT THE SCHOOL CONCERT
Her eyes were blue,
blonde hair tied in plaits -
a blue hair band.
Her blue pleated skirt flew
behind her as she danced
in white socks-

Yvan and I played synthesisers,
Rachel stood and listened
She put an arm around me and said,
'Well done!'
'Do you think so?'' I said.
'Let's talk,' she said.
Tony Anderson, Stroke and Brain Injury Rehab Unit, City Hospital,
Truro

EXERCISE 19

Subject: 'Garden poem'
Notes: Boundervean on a sunny day. We sat in the garden as it
was such a lovely day. Mary has done a lot of work to the pond
and the planting around it. They have all helped to make this
garden. I suggested we write about a garden.
Describe a favourite or well-known garden, yard or patio.
Choose a particular moment in the garden.
Who are you with - are you alone?
Are there trees? Name them, and describe the leaves, trunks,
flowers.
Are there flower beds? What are the flowers?
Is there grass? Is it brown, yellow, green, short, long. Are there
grass seeds?
Are there insects? What? What are they doing? Butterflies flitting,
midges biting, a seething ants' nest, mosquitoes whining, flies dive
bombing; wasps stinging, settling
on the picnic lunch; bees hovering over a red fuchsia flower? How
do you feel?

FISH POND
Oh fish! You are so nice
Swimming in the pond.
You are full of grace.
How much I would give
To be a fish.

Fish, fish, you are so nice
I think of you at night.
MaryPhillips,Boundervean.

EXERCISE 20

Subject: 'I am an animal'
Notes: Write as if you are an animal, bird, fish or insect.
First lines - where are you and what are you doing? Elaborate and
be specific not general.
e.g. - climb a coconut palm;
I am hiding under a big flat black stone;
I float in a water-lily filled garden pond;
I creep along a leafy forest floor where no light reaches the damp
and bosky earth.
I swing from a tall tree in a rain forest;
I am curled up in the sun on a soft cushion by the window;
I soar above snow covered craggy mountains.
Next lines-what do you see and what are you going to do?
    e.g. A velvet vole darts
and I swoop to take it in my talons;
My boy strokes my fur.
I open one eye and purr;
A sudden fury of water
a flurry of mud hides me.
I am still as a stone
The pike glides away.

CAT FEELING LAZY
I'm lying in the sun
feeling lazy.
I saw a mouse
under the seat
but I'm too lazy,
I'd rather sleep.
Marjorie Pakes, Stroke Rehab Unit

69

SLITHERING

I am a snake hiding among
the long tall grass.
I can climb trees,
camouflage myself
I eat all insects and
things in trees.
I'll tell you something -
I wouldn't eat those blasted
wasps or bees -
they sting, they do 'urt -
those bleddy things.
Gary Gibson, Boundervean

EXERCISE 21

Subject: 'On the shelf'
Notes:Choose a collection of objects - ornaments, books,
photographs, mementoes, souvenirs you know intimately. Perhaps
they are arranged on a bookshelf, a mantelpiece, a desk, or in a
glazed cabinet. Now or in your past.
Describe each item fully and say why it has importance to you.
Which room?
Is it a shelf of wood, a mantelpiece of marble; a book case?
What is on the shelf?
Why have you kept the object?
Who gave it to you;
Or where did you find it? Elaborate.
Colour, shape, reminds you of?
Write as much as you can about each item. Go off on a tangent,
ramble on about whatever comes into your mind when you think

of that object. You will find that you will probably end up with a
piece about yourself and your past and your feelings.

ON THE SHELF
On the book shelf I made
is a small soft toy, Leo the lion
I was a young lion in Leo's Club.

A large ashtray, Murano glass,
Heavy, round, whiskey coloured
Reminds me of Max of Milano,
my old friend and partner -
Flamboyant in his naughtiness.

A calendar front from 1985 -
A picture of Mousehole harbour at high tide,
Small fishing boats moored close,
Steep hills, houses like a pack of cards
To remind me of home.

The year before, in London
I went blind
Survived at work for a while
But then came home.
Martin Coade, Marie Therese House, Hayle

THE FOURTEENTH CENTURY CHEST
I gaze at you and think of bold
black, dark, something old,
thick long arch panels wide
cut, carved with lunate sides.

Upon your age you do support
sins or battles lost and fought.
Scarred, burnt, seared through time
with loving hands reclaimed to mine.

71

Now they sit all passions spent
helmets from the warriors heads,
gauntlets brown with fingers gone,
chain mail in heavy pile
with their secret still inside.
Barbara Faragher, Marie Therese House, Hayle

EXERCISE 22

Subject: 'I wake at night'
Note: Write a six line poem beginning with I WAKE AT NIGHT,
or have the phrase as the theme. Fears are often worse in the
night. A dream may have woken you. The night is long when you
are unhappy or ill. Read poems by Derek Mahon and Dick Davis
about being awake at night.

ABSENCE
from *Light Music*

I wake at night
in a house white
with moonlight.

Somewhere my son
his vigour, his laughter;
Somewhere my daughter.
Derek Mahon (b 1941)

SIX A.M. THOUGHTS

As soon as you wake they come blundering in
Like puppies or importunate children;
What was a landscape emerging from mist
Becomes at once a disordered garden.

And the mess they trail with them! Embarrassments,
Anger, lust, fear - in fact the whole pig-pen
And who'll clean it up? No hope for sleep now -
Just heave yourself out, make the tea, and give in.
by Dick Davis (b1945 -)

DRAMA AT NIGHT

A summer night, windows wide
I woke to the sound of
maroons summoning the lifeboat.
One explosion then another.

The seagulls also woken
fly - screeching and calling -
white flying shapes
ghostly against the dark sky.

I lay and thought of the
unfolding drama out at sea,
of the terror and fear and danger
of those at the mercy of the sea.

I feared for them and prayed
for them and then
went back to sleep.
Anne Noonan, Marie Therese House

I WOKE AT NIGHT
The wind at the doors
blowing around,
banging the gate
making a row in the oak.
The barn owl going 'Ow, ow.'
Honeysuckle, a lovely smell
through the bedroom window.

Waves crashing on the rocky shore
at Pentuan where we walked
together, Pauline and I
and saw blue butterflies,
a small brown fox in broad daylight
the colour of bracken.
Heather, foxgloves, gorse.
I am happy.
David Westaway, Marie Therese House

Note: A day on the Stroke Rehab Unit. Paul wants to write about
something that has been troubling him - a patient he had
comforted in the night left this morning before he could say
goodbye. Marjorie is so positive! Insisted on writing something
cheerful - 'You don't always want to think of sad things!'

I WAKE AT NIGHT
I wake at night
thinking of the lovely day
we saw the seagull flying with the sky,
wish we could also be a seagull able to fly.

We saw children
with warmth on their backs
digging in the sand,
their little feet, their hands.
Marjorie Pakes, Stroke Rehab Unit.

CHRIS
You were to be transferred
to Putney -
they could help you more.
You can't speak
but you cried
frightened.

For nearly an hour
I'd held your hand,
promised to be there
when you went.
I'd woken again,
heard you near.

Next morning, early,
as they'd cleaned you up
I'd gone to wash,
came back -
you'd gone.
Paul Hoskin, Stroke and Brain Injury Rehab Unit, Truro

Note: One of the nurses said she knew which hospital Chris had
been transferred to and she would see that he received a copy of
Paul's poem.

I WOKE AT NIGHT
I woke at night
could see no light
my eyes were open
yet there was still night.

With fear
I felt or something near
it was not right for me
that I could not see.

When I woke up true
I did find
it was still night
and I was blind.
Martin Coade, Marie Therese Unit, Hayle

EXERCISE 23

Subject: 'Your job'
Notes: Tell us about it in detail.
The name of the place where you work or worked.
The place - a garage, a post office, a shop, an office, an old
people's home; a school;
an airport; a beach; a ship; a public house; local council; lifeboat
house; building site.
ATMOSPHERE - elaborate and be precise and write as much as
you can about the atmosphere.
        Describe what you did. - the actual process.
Alone or with other people?
How did you feel?
Describe the smell of your place of work. Burning, bread cooking,
farm smells, animals.
The sounds – machine or man-made.
Any detail of the method you used for your work – show us in
words exactly what you experienced.

BAKERS SHOP, ST IVES
Fry donuts crispy,
in town, so much effort,
sometimes we never seemed so busy.
Pasties and sweet cakes in the morning
and decorate each - it was hot.
There were different - so many smells -
saffron cakes, lardy cakes,
strawberry, raspberry.
It was so hot.
Paula Fowler, Marie Therese House

A DAY AT THE MUSEUM OF GEOLOGY
The air is cool controlled
the atmosphere quiet.
Silence enfolds the exhibits,
 the rocks and their minerals are held
silent, frozen in glass,
glowing colours hinting at their
violent, colourful past.
Fossils of all shades, sizes give
tantalising glimpses of past times.
Suddenly a door bangs
voices high and loud fill the air.
The sound of many feet running up
stone steps drowns the silence.
Lights flood the area.
Excited shouts and laughter
bounce off walls.
The rocks and fossils seem to preen
to attract the greatest crowd
and for the duration of the visit take on
a renewed power and live again.
Clutching books, rocks, fossils,
the children depart slowly
down the stone stairway.
The door closes.
Darkness comes,
silence descends,
exhibits rest.
Barbara Faragher, Marie Therese House

EXERCISE 24

Subject: 'Acrostic'
Notes: Claire, who was knocked off her bike by a car and suffered head injuries, wrote about her sons, Thomas and Mathias, and then wrote another acrostic about her husband, Andy. The acrostic was her own idea. Acrostics use each letter of the subject or title as the first letter of each line of the poem. This is a good exercise as it limits and challenges writers to find exactly the right word.

THOMAS
Too much
Himself at times, at
Other times my son, or
Matty's big brother, or even
Andy when young;
Sometimes just a small boy.

MATHIAS
Mathias is
Absolutely
True to
Himself.
If he is sometimes
Aggravatingly clever for a six year old
So be it.

ANDY
Andy is everything to me;
Nothing would matter very much if he were
Dead or living with someone else.
You might think it strange but it's just the way it is.
Claire Sexton, Rehab Unit.

EXERCISE 25

Subject: 'Food'
Notes: This is a good exercise to do if all others fail! Maybe no one wants to write about their life or their mother or their work.Food is always of interest to everyone, even people who have to drink through a straw
use the subject of food or drink as a trigger for a poem.
Are you hungry?
What is your favourite food?
Think about a memorable meal with friends, lover, family.
Cooking for yourself or someone else - a crowd.
Sunday dinners.
A restaurant meal.
Snacks, drink, sweets, puddings, foreign food- take away food.
Let the trigger - Food - enable you to write about anything else that might come into your head.

THE MACKEREL
The fish that almost swam
Through my fingers

lies here motionless
The skin no longer rainbows,

The eyes no longer
As big as the sea

Just to be food for us
The fish that wouldn't be able

To almost escape with
Such insouciance

Or be so beautiful
In early death.
Clare Sexton. Stroke Rehab Unit

Note: Barbara Faragher was the only writer today. She had written homework based on the suggested theme of FOOD, and then told me about something she had seen yesterday, and I suggested she write it down as a poem.

A GRANDFATHER, AN IMMACULATELY DRESSED BABY AND A CHOCOLATE CAKE.

'My Persil-white darling,, my sweetheart,
you'll have the gooiest chocolate cake.'
                    'We want a cake,
a sticky chocolate cake,
No, no, not that one, sweetheart,
more chocolate, more cream.
Yes, that one with the cherry.
No, we don't want a bag.
Yes, you'll have it sweetheart.
Take a bite.
Yes, lick your fingers.
It's running down your frock.
That's right, hold on to your lovely white hat.
Won't Mummy be pleased –
all that lovely chocolate running down.
It's in your hair, around your mouth.
Lovely!'
Barbara Faragher, Marie Therese House.

MY CHOCOLATE LOVER

From daylight to darkening fall of night
you tempt me. The sight, the scent,
 the loving feel of you upon my tongue.
One lick, one bite, sheer delight, you melt
in my mouth, flow softly sweetly down
my chocolate lover.
Everywhere I look you are there,
forcing me to view you in all your glory,
bedecked with jewels of glittering fruit,
surrounded in light fluffy white cream.

80

Evening time, at last we are alone.
Slowly, guiltily, my fingers open your cold silver foil.
Naked you lay before me, dark, smooth,
bitter sweet. Once again I take you
my chocolate lover.
Barbara Faragher, Marie Therese House

FOOD
I remember catching shrimps,
we ate them for tea on one of our
summer holidays in a rented chalet on the beach.
It's cruel how they are caught and eaten.
I'd not cook them myself.

Christmas
I looked for the silver sixpences
in the Christmas pudding.
Delicious! I looked forward to this.

I remember learning to cook.
I cooked for six with the help of one other person.
I got the food out of the oven
and I dropped it on the floor.
I said, 'Can the dog have it?'
We opened a tin.

Another occasion I boiled a pudding
dry on the stove whilst I drank tea outside.
But at Tolvean I learned to cook quite well.
We made stews.
Bovril and Marmite went into them.
I cooked a chicken and tried to put stuffing
in the wrong part of it.
I have good memories of Tolvean and cooking.
Shirley Lillie, Boundervean

EXERCISE 26

Subject: 'An enjoyable pastime'
Notes: Write about something you enjoy doing or did before you were ill. This exercise is usually a good way of getting to know people. What you see with very sick patients is not the real person - a disabled person in a wheelchair – perhaps paralysed, unable to hold a pen in their right hand; needing help to do every little thing. The real person is still there inside, needing to be recognised, wanting confirmation of who he or she is. This exercise is a way the writer can communicate experience.

What hobby or pastime, sport, game, activity did you enjoy? Walking; swimming; bowls; cricket; gardening; bird watching; playing with a grandchild; antique collecting; acting; dancing; painting; greyhound racing; horse riding; going to car boot sales. Describe the actual method of doing what you did.
Read 'Naming of Parts' by Herbert Read to illustrate the power of detail in a poem.
Tell us how you felt.
Where did you do this?
Were you alone or with a group?
What did you hear?
What did you see?
What equipment did you use?
Describe it.
Blow by blow account of what you did.
Be specific. Do not generalise.
Write it in the present as if if you are actually doing it now.
Enthuse!

FLY FISHING
The whisper of the leader as it passes through the ferrules,
taking with it the fly or nymph to its target fish.
On the warm day when the mayfly hatch gets under way
and the fat trout swirls and disturbs
the surface as he decides to take your fly.
The strike, the play and then the desperate
thrashing as he succumbs to his tiredness.

Do I need him? No! Gently does it, no damage.
Such a lightweight leader.
What a beauty he is - about three and a half pounds.
Back you go, my handsome, and try a live mayfly.
Graham Gratton, StrokeRehab Unit

GOLF AT KILLIOW PARK

It is early on Saturday morning.
The first tee is free and we are ready to start our game.
The rain clouds that threaten to spoil the morning have not yet
stopped overhead
and the sun in is trying so hard to shine through the darkened
sky.
The grass is green and well-cropped and there is the smell of new
mown grass in
the air.

The clay hills of St Austell are visible on the skyline as is the tower
of Probus Church
which peeks out above the trees.
The distant hum of traffic on the busy road to Falmouth does not
detract us.
We select a ball from the bag and set it on a tee peg.
What club shall I select?
Will today be that long hoped for day when everything will go
right and my game will
come together to enable me to produce a low scoring round?

Does it really matter?
The birds are singing in the trees and the squirrels chase their
tails on the ground under the trees.

We are ready. Don't rush. Relax and let the club do the work
A smooth swing and contact will put the ball down the fairway,
toward the green and
the pole holding the flag over the first hole.
My friend is to tee off first . The chatter stops.

Now comes the time to put into practice what we have been taught
and practised.
Address the ball, making sure that the feet are in the correct
position.
Hit through the ball, the club head in a straight line to the flag.
Don't rush or jerk.
Make the swing smooth, keep the knees straight.

Will I have the balance to do this again?
Will the swing take me off balance –
the effort will have to come from a smooth swing or else I will be
off balance,
could fall like a horse falling at the first fence.
Roy Glanville, Stroke Rehab Unit

IN THE CHORUS
The costumes
the makeup
the orchestra tuning up
the stage manager setting the scenery.
To walk on in front of a thousand people,
 to hear the applause.
The lights are very bright
but you take no notice of the heat.
The leading lady and man full of nerves -
their thoughts - Will I remember my lines?

Fiddler on the Roof- Cossack dancing;
Oklahoma - tap dancing -
the enjoyment of it
now seems- just a dream.
I took it all for granted
not knowing what the future held.
Peter Kemp, Rehab Unit, City Hospital

29th July 97 Marie Therese House
Notes: Quiet room was occupied so we sat in the conservatory.
Sue is a keen poet who enters competitions regularly and hopes
to publish a volume of poetry one day.
Ann is Scottish, and has lived in South Africa, Zambia and
Nigeria. Ann said she had enjoyed a wonderful life in Africa with
two engineer husbands, as MS had not affected her until 1980.
She is very good looking and looks healthy. She says people
cannot believe she has to be in a wheelchair.
I asked the workshop writers about hobbies, favourite sports or
activities now or in the past. We talked about their choices and
made decisions about which would make interesting subjects for
a poem. Sue wanted to write about the death of her dog - walking
the dog being the hobby. She had written it before and was trying
to remember it. She likes rhyming couplets. She worked on it in
the workshop and said she would finish it later. She is here for a
week, so I won't see her next Tuesday, but she will be back. She
talked about her father dying her arms as the dog had done. I
suggested she write about her father within the dog walking poem.
She will try. She recounted an occasion when he embarrassed
her as a schoolgirl and she might write about that. Ann Mackay
could not write so I scribed for her. Barbara had been a keen
javelin thrower and she had done homework - about a hot summer
as a child.

TENNIS IN AFRICA
I am an unorthodox player.
They'd say to me,
'Could you not hit the ball harder?'
'Put all your force behind hitting the service ball.'
'I don't have a very strong wrist.' I'd say,
so it barely managed to get in the right court.

Then I would surprise them
by hitting a very hard one
and sometimes miss on a return
and other times hit a fabulous one
straight down the line.

I had lots of little white dresses.
I had a Fred Perry pleated skirt,
wrapped over at the waist band, quite sexy.
I made a little white dress with
a broad zip down the front - quite sexy,
to distract the male players.

My dark hair was well cut
so it swung as I ran about the court.
Warm wind, Kaffiabo trees flat on top like a table.
My womanising partner who looked like Tony Perkins,
(a traffic cop on a motorbike) said -
'You may not be the best tennis player, Ann,
but you're the prettiest.'
Ann Mackay, Marie Therese House.

BEAN STICKS TO JAVELIN
No playing Field, just a cleared bomb-site.
No equipment, just a bundle of bean-sticks.

Take a bean-stick,
tuck it under your arm,
throw it.

I pounded the ground
with running feet
threw the stick.
It clattered to earth
with a crack.

After a year of bean-sticks
the javelin was light.
I stood arm raised high,
brought the shining shaft back.
Up it went, caught the light, point impacted in the soft damp earth,
its tail quivered, danced.
Barbara Faragher, Marie Therese House

Note: After the workshop had finished Barbara thanked me, saying that she really enjoyed and looked forward to the sessions. And even when she was feeling unwell and did not really want to make the effort to come to Marie Therese, she came anyway when she knew I would be there. She also thought the others benefited - "it was like a comedy programme" and it cheered her up. She always felt better for having done a workshop. She thought it especially helped MS sufferers because they were often subject to severe mood changes.

KNIGHT OF MUSIC

When I get on stage I feel the part.
I dress in a white jump suit like Elvis wore.
I also have bought about £180 worth of jewellery.
I have one silver ring, one gold, and a red garnet ring,
a gold bracelet, plus a heavy gold chain
with a cross with a silver setting.
The atmosphere is fantastic,
people taking photographs while I'm singing.,
having their photos taken with me,
ladies wanting to dance with me.
I hold the mike -
'The Wonder of You,'
'My Way,' 'Are You Lonesome Tonight?'
'Blue Suede Shoes,' 'All Shook Up.'
Gary Gibson, Boundervean

Notes: A get-together on the Rehab Unit with Pat Clarke, Peter Kemp, Chris Pearson, David Wills, Lisa Wills. *The Remedy* - Cornwall Clinical Journal - publishes the occasional poem from the Poetry Remedy workshops. I read out Dorothy Biddick's published poem from this quarter's *Remedy*. Gave a copy to Gordon, the physiotherapist, to post to her.

It was Peter Kemp's last workshop as he is leaving on Monday. A friend is going to move in with him and look after him. Such a gentle man, I hope he does well. He said it had been very enjoyable doing the workshops, and he never thought he would be able to do what he has done. He wants to keep in touch with me, he said. Unfortunately, half way through the session he was whisked off to do a hoist exercise and he had to go. I asked him to do the homework of a childhood memory. He said he would post it to me.

Pat Clarke has had her piece of missing skull replaced and her hair is growing in spikes over her well-shaped head and enormous stitched scar. She is great. So lively and sociable. She says she will miss the company of people here in the rehab unit when she goes home.

Teenager Lisa Wills is always on the stroke rehab ward to help look after her grandfather - a lovely Cornishman. He holds her hand, smiles at her. She takes him off to the bathroom, encourages him to write when he falters.

The first session with him, he simply wrote -

Dear Lisa
I miss you
so when
you are not here

EXERCISE 27

Subject: 'Home'
Notes: Home can be your present home, your parents' or grandparents' home; a loved house.
Pretend you are going through your garden gate.
Describe the sounds you hear - e.g. - a black bird singing; telegraph wires humming, waves crashing; music; children shouting.
Go in the door into the house. What colour is it? Has it peeling paint? Is there a knocker or a bell? Do you ring it or walk straight in. Do you turn the key?
Inside the house -
Describe the scents and smells - cooking? What is cooking? Roast beef, a cake; fried onions. Flowers - honeysuckle, roses. Be specific always, not vague. Never flowers but cornflowers, forget-me-nots, daffodils. Give things their names. We can see and smell them better.
What do you see? Flock wallpaper? Antique bureau?; a box of vegetables rotting in the corner?
What happens? Cat leaps; dog barks; a chair scrapes.
Who is there? What is he doing?
Family? Sit around a table, eat together?
Sit and talk, laugh play cards. Read.
On the wall there is a picture, photo, cards, calendar. Clock.
Furniture? Sofa with a cat on a tapestry cushion.
Real cat on tapestry cat. Knitting in a bag, sewing things, chess set on table, books on the wall.
Describe the things you remember. Relive time spent in a beloved grandparents or friend's home. Enjoy the memory.

46 OAKFIELD RD., FALMOUTH
From my room I see the river Fal,
fishy smells come through the open window,
I see people passing to All Saints Church
beyond the garden hedge.

By the fire - Sabre - our puppy.
Andrew and Sue at their homework.
I slide on a blue rug on the lino.
From the kitchen my mother shouts
'Don't do that,' and
'don't argue with your brother.'

My brother calls me 'Fattie.'
I sit in the window and
dream of elephants
bigger and fatter than me
who will flatten him.
Philippa Vinson, Marie Therese House, Hayle

HOME
Four Lanes way,
Cornish hedges,
Carn Brea.
It's beautiful.
I was brought up there
with my mum and dad.
He was in Cornish meat,
Ernest Nicholas.
Mum could be a nuisance occasionally,
she had her moments - Phyllis.

Used to go up to the Carn,
cut thistles,
Dad had a farm.
Cows, pigs, horses.
Mum made pasties -
mainly good beef,
turnips, onions, potatoes, parsley .
We had a dog, a collie, Benjie.
I loved cooking,
cutting thistles down
with a scythe,
I was eleven. *Rosemary Bottrell, St Julia's Hospice, Hayle*

CARN BREA
I live in my Gran's old house.
I remember the wind
I hear the slates banging on the roof,
a couple are loose.

Used to walk up there,
lived in Redruth,
never had a car -
only a couple of miles away.

Gran's cakes
especially Christmas cakes,
Didn't like them
but I remember them.
Silver balls on the cakes.
I used to think they were ball bearings.
Yeast buns, didn't like them either.
Didn't like raisins or currents, either.
Used to be very warm,
used to have the Rayburn going.
We've got Economy Seven now,
it's easier to look after.
Johnny Bottrell (Rosemary Bottrell's son who was visiting her.)

THE FARM AT MAWNAN SMITH
Dairy cows, beef cows, sheep. I loved them all.
We had to grind the barley every week for their feed.
I had to give it up eventually.
I grew out of the capacity to be able to do the things
the awful things you have to do to them.

I had all the rescue animals, sick cows with abscesses,
mastitis - they responded to healing.
Lambsy, the sheep, used to bring in everybody if they got chased
by dogs.
He came thundering in usually with a few companions.

Five dogs in the caravan with us and the odd cat, who lived with
the birds.

A marvellous crow, a rook, Peter brought in one day,
found under a bush, a very young bird.
He'd sit on top of the water boiler,
then on top of the door,
took most of the wallpaper off.
He used to fly overhead when I was on my bicycle.

Used to try and come into the shops
and I'd have to shut him out.
He'd hang on the door handle and flap.
He was marvellous - Dry Gulch he was called,
used to take you from behind, you see,
 an absolute menace, one of my favourite animals,
lived with us for five years.

Used to spread the pay packet money all over the yard.
Used to take Peter's watch and hide it in the hay.
And then a magpie dropped out of the sky
into five year old David's hand.
Jenny Rickard, St Julia's Hospice, Hayle.

Note: Twelve hospice carers - nurses, volunteers, auxiliary nurses,
a priest and a bereavement councillor attended a workshop in the
day room at the hospice. I gave them all paper and pens. They
were provided with clipboards. They sat in a circle in the
dayroom. I asked them to introduce themselves and write their
name at the top of their paper. Read some workshop 'Home
Poems'.
        Write about your home as a child, or now, or your
grandparents' home or your
parents' home.
I want to know the address the area, the view from the windows.

Start - Go through the gate into the garden.
What grows in it? Name the plants and trees.

Paths, steps, pond?

Open the door and go inside. Perhaps your mother is cooking, what smells are there?

Is there steam, smoke, scent of sweet peas, cabbage?

Describe pictures on the walls, furniture, carpets, floors, ceilings, high, low.

Did you bang your head?

Were you frightened of the witch in the hall cupboard or the dog growling?

Is the cat asleep? Does it purr in the sunny window scat?

Is there a baby crying or a radio playing the ARCHERS theme tune?

Does your father read the newspaper, do the pools, do a jigsaw?

What is there for tea, or lunch, inside or out, on a pine table, mahogany, checked tablecloth?

What are the ornaments - china dogs, ship's bell, silver plate, pictures by children.

Are there crumpets still for tea?

What does your mother/grandmother say? Think of a phrase she used, or something she always did - rubbed her nose with her thumb, hid her sweets under a cushion, folded over the corner of the page of her book.

Did she sew, knit, did she make rag rugs, cook, love the garden. Describe what they did in detail.

If she made toys, describe one of them, or describe her cleaning shoes, crocheting embroidering an antimacassar.

Smells, sights, touch, sounds, taste.

The smell of apples cooking, the cold custard congealing on the bowl of tinned fruit.

The softness of the chenille table cloth, put on to protect it from sticky fingers and knocks.

The rough chin, unshaved, tobacco breath, a wet kiss.

If you cannot get started or do not want to describe the garden- start with the line -Sunday, a hot summer's day - or - a dark sky full of snow, or - There she/he is, ... or I open the gate... or - The kettle whistles; or- the Scottie dog barks; or - Her blue apron is covered in floury smears; etc.

Write for ten minutes - these are notes - this is not yet a poem, probably.

Before you write your own poem - please do not use rhymes unless they are accidental, or half rhymes, do not think of getting words to rhyme, think more of telling the truth, simply, and leave out complicated explanations.

I get them all to read out their notes. No one expects brilliant pieces of work, this is a first draught. I make notes as they read. I praise details from each piece.

Get them to delete unimportant words - select the good detail and underline.

Write a new draft, on another page write page 2 on it and your name.

Work for five minutes.

Read out again.

Do a copy and give one to me and keep the other.

If someone reads badly, do it for them, show them the strengths of their writing suggest line-end changes if necessary.

As with the patients I take home the rough drafts and type them and print them and return them to the writer.

I always ask their permission to read out the piece or use their work on a poster or for a publication.

LATE AFTERNOON IN STENNACK.
The water chute as I come round the corner -
The buzzards mewing overhead,
The robin singing in the hawthorn,
The crunch of the gravel as I push
The bike through the brown gate.
The water pump spilling over the kitchen pond -
The ringed dove's rapid flutter of wings
And the whirr of the telegraph wire,
The back door swings open,
Releasing the smell of Aga fumes
Which drift through the air.
Run and open the window and
fresh air flows in -
Whistler squeals with pleasure

Jumping on his back legs to greet me.
Put the kettle on the Aga,
Cup and saucer, tea bag and milk
Two digestive biscuits.
Whistler hears the tin rattle,
Bustles in for his share.

Peace, quiet, still,
So pleasant
It just seems to wash over me.
Telegraph crossword - will it be easy today?
Look at the kitchen clock -
Not time for George to be home.
Relax for a few minutes.
What will we have for supper?
The telephone bell rings sharply
Shattering the peace.
Is George home yet?
Is he on duty tonight?
Trouble with the sheep again.
Plates clatter, saucepans clang,
Cutlery, mats, six o'clock news.
Sound of wheels on the gravel,
Slam of car door,
George's cough as he opens the door.
Had a busy day?
Like a glass of wine?
Supper in ten minutes - Okay?
Anne Blake, St Julia's Hospice

FARMHOUSE IN TIPPERARY
Home - a place for happiness
Children to share happy times, sad times,
Meal times, specially
To share these moments.
Remembering times past.
The creaking door from hall to kitchen.
The wind whispering in the tall pines

95

That surround the old house.
The old black range, the only source of heat
in the rambling place,
kettle steaming on the hob.
The rain patters on the galvanised roof.
The smell of soda bread, cow dung and new-mown hay.
The can of sweet tea taken to the men in the meadow.

The view from the bedroom window of the full moon
Rising high behind the mountains.
Aunty Kate - you funny old dear, crotchety and cross.
Grey hair, walking stick waiting at the corner of the house.
Come to get us as we come flying past.
Whack!
But later I wonder what it was that made you
Eccentric, aloof and a Miss.
A broken heart.
You waited and waited but he never returned.
He did not know you waited.
Cathy Davey, St Julia's Hospice

Notes: Today on the Rehab Unit
Rosemary brought in Janet, a grey-haired Down's Syndrome lady
whose birthday it was yesterday and scribed for her.
Leon is cheerful about going home at the weekend for three days
then going out for good next Friday, hopefully. Trudie - physio
assistant joined in and scribed for Jean Jeanette was there too.
We read out their last efforts which they were pleased with.
Trudy has earthy humour and we had an hilarious session. First
time Jean has not sobbed.

HOME
Neighbours talking
cockateels squawking
kettle boiling -
the click as it turns itself off.
The mower working.
My porcelain dolls

the blue and white china tea set
with Charles and Diana on.

The smell of chicken roasting,
cauliflower, cabbage, carrots, parsnips,
onion and potatoes. Yorkshire pudding.

In the garden a bird bath.
Thrushes, starlings, bluetits,
the occasional robin.
 he smell of roses - red, white, yellow
that my auntie Ritta gave me before she died.

My son Mark, he's twenty-six,
looks like his father -
six foot tall, dark hair, blue eyes -
a Cornishman.
Jeanette Thomas, Stroke Rehab Unit

HOME
The radio playing Cliff Richard
My dad talking to me,
cars passing by,
wind whispering through the trees.

I see my dad and my records
and my bedroom with my Cliff Richard records and tapes,
and I see my dad making me
pasties for my lunch.
I love my Dad and my sisters and brothers.
My sister Marian made me a lovely Birthday cake
and I had lots of cards and presents.
I had a lovely Birthday.
Janet Creddy, Rehab Unit, City Hospital, Truro

Note:. Jeanette was unhappy because of what had happened on
her weekend home. I got her to talk about it and write it down as
if it was a scene from a play.

HOME FROM THE HOSPITAL FOR A WEEKEND
Mark - I am going fishing with my sister.
Me - You're selfish, Mark, because you know
your father can't take me out without help.
Mark - She is my sister. Can't I see her?
Me - But you can see her all week.
Mark - But I'm going.
He went.
Lance - You shouldn't have said that.
Me - I know that.
Jeanette Thomas, Rehab Unit, City Hospital

EXERCISE 28

Subject: 'Things I like'
Note: Read out Patricia Heaney's poem 'Things I like' from
Lifelines 2.

THINGS I LIKE
Bark of our dog to welcome us home,
Croak of a frog on the commons;
Trot of a horse,
Heather and gorse on Bellewstown hill;
Bleat of a lamb,
Gurgling and laughing of Curley's baby
In her pram.
Patricia Heaney (born c1962)

Note: I had worked with Paula on her own and she wanted to
come to the next workshop at Marie Therese. It had been very
difficult getting her to talk or write. Saw her on her own again on
May 7th.
Paula did her own writing this time, slowly and with many halts
but with encouragement and urging she completed a poem. One
line was a joint effort because neither of us could read back what
she had written and she could not think what it was either.
I'll show you the process - how I got the result.

THINGS I LIKE
Paula - The things I like - the beach.
Me - What sort of' weather do you like?
Paula - Sunny weather.
Me - What do you like doing in sunny weather?
Paula - Lying on the beach.
Me - What can you see on the beach?
Paula - People on the beach.
Me - What sounds do you hear?
Paula - The river it seems to make a noise.
People laughing.
Me - What smells are there?
Paula - Fish and chips.
People trying (lying in the sun) - (joint effort)
people laughing
people laugh
and I swim along.
Me - what else do you like - something completely different?
Paula - Gin with ice.

So, the finished poem was -

THE BEACH
I like the beach,
sunny weather
lying on the beach.
People on the beach.
The river it seems
to make a noise
people laughing.
Fish and chips.
People trying lying in the sun.
People laughing
people laugh
and I swim along.
and I like gin and tonic.
Paula Fowler

AND THEN MAKING BREAD FOR TEA
Sounds of the blackbird and pheasant
in the early morning.
Walking in the Highlands,
climbing through the pine forest
to the mountain top -
seeing the shy red deer,
hearing the mating stag calling.
Arriving home pleasantly tired
to make hot drinks for everyone.

And then making bread for tea.
Setting the yeast and liquid
into a warm place to rise
to a foaming mass before
adding to the flour and
kneading with vigour
releasing all my pent up tensions
before shaping it and then cooking it.
Sitting by an open fire.
The owl hunting and returning
to the barn at dusk.
Jeanette Green, Marie Therese House

THINGS I LIKE
A winter's night,
to be warm and hear
the wind outside,
to feel safe.
    To hear snow and silence -
    it wakes you it's so still.
To sit in the garden
with the smell of roses
and sun on my back
to walk in the autumn
crunching leaves under my feet,
shiny new conkers.

100

Early morning in the spring
has a special scent,
everything so fresh,
birds building their nests
rush in and out so many times
to feed the young.
Young birds look at their new life.
Marjorie Pakes, Rehab Unit, City Hospital

EXERCISE 29

Subject: A group exercise – a good moan about 'Things we don't
like'

THE WELL-MEANERS
'Be patient, it will all come in time.'
'Think how lucky you are.'
'Think about poor old so-and-so.'
'Someone's always worse off than you.'

They are walking and I am not -
'Give it time.'

What annoys me -
'How is he?'
'Is he better?'
'Does he take sugar?'
They don't talk to you.

'You are going to be all right.'
Your are not going to be all right.
You want them - the doctors - to say
you will be much better in six months.
You want them to go out on a limb
and tell you what really will happen
(but only if it's good.)
*Peter Kemp, Chris Pearson, Roy Glanville, David Wills, Nyall
Samper, Stroke Rehab Unit.*

EXERCISE 30

Subject: 'Party or special occasion'
Note: I start by asking if the writers have ever been to a dance
or party?
Choose an important or memorable occasion e.g. a Surprise party,
a Birthday party, a wedding party; your first dance.
We discuss the party.
What did you see, hear, smell, taste, touch, feel? Describe the
setting. Outside, a ballroom, a smoky dive.
Tell me about the food and drinks.
Was there music? What music? Big bands, jazz, records, Beatles,
Old Time dancing?
A DJ?
What clothes did you wear - chiffon, silk, full skirts, pleated,
stockings, suspenders? Do you remember dance tunes, the
names?
Who else was there?
What words were spoken?

SIXTEEN, AT MY FIRST DANCE, MAURIPUR, KARACHI
I wore a long white dress, silky with net on top,
red velvet ribbon slotted round the neck,
bare arms and neck,
sandals on bare feet.
The sergeants' mess dingily lit
with chairs and tables around the room,
the six musicians in one corner -
'Tennessee Waltz', 'You Belong to Me.'

Drinks from the bar.
The smell of Pakistan -
dust, shit, spice, French chalk.
Danced and danced with tall ones, short ones,
redheads, blondes, baldies, young enough
and old enough to be my brother or grandfather.
Everyone steaming, smooching,

clagged together at the cheek.
One chap said it was like dancing
with a Sherman tank -
I tried harder after that.
Dorothy Biddick, Stroke Rehab Unit, City Hospital, Truro, Cornwall

THE OPENING PARTY
Pam Nestorovic,
a little autumn brunette
wore a tight blue skirt
of evening sunshine blue
and fitted perfectly in my arms
as I bent below the beams
on the paddle steamer Medway Queen.

We danced to San Francisco
kissed the flowers from her hair,
we went up to the starlit deck
to taste champagne and the cool Medina air.
Martin Coade, Marie Therese House, Hayle

Note: Martin died in March 1997 I gave his eighty-seven year
old mother, who has been looking after him for the last ten years,
his entire output of work from the workshops. At the next
workshop I read the best of his poems to the other writers. There
were two new people and they said they wished they had known
him. I got everyone to introduce themselves and tell us something
of their history. This is a good way for the group to get to know
each other. Kerry is a frail, beautiful twenty three year old who
controls her hi-tech wheelchair with a finger of one hand.

SUNSET PARTY
Samantha, a friend; Judith, my foster sister,
Then others appeared on the sandy beach
Wearing shorts, T-shirts, and I was
Wearing striped shorts, blue and green,
A light green top.

103

They had fun in the water, surfing, swimming,
We chatted.
Some of' the boys had long hair and surf boards.
A warm day, blue sky reflected in the water.
The sun was falling,
We talked of life, boys, Newquay clubs,
Pubs, dances, fun, romances.
The sea swallowed the sun.
Kerry Jackson, Marie Therese House

SURPRISE
Balloons and tinsel flying around, Even some
on the ground.
Mary at the top of the stairs
with confetti.
John looking out the
window for Jan,
Me with my camera in hand.
John said - 'She's here!'
So I hit the ground.
Door opens,
Jan steps in.
Flash! Got ya!
Keep coming this way.
Confetti hit her.
Gary Gibson, Boundervean

CHRISTMAS
Our neighbours gave me a doll's pram.
I pushed my brothers and sister around in it
until it got broken:
Mum could not afford a doll.
One Christmas we had yellow

Tonka lorries each.
We used to ride them down the burrows.
We made roads in the garden.
Mum came out with pasties
she had made that morning,
each in a white paper bag.
Mum and Dad sat with us
in a big circle to eat.
We had home-made sherbet
lemonade in our cups.
Jeannette Thomas, Stroke Rehab Unit City Hospital, Truro.

EXERCISE 31

Subject: 'I hold up an object'
Note: I held up an object and asked them to write for ten minutes
about it. It was my metal seagull-carrying-a-fish brooch that my
daughter made. The two writers produced finished pieces in ten
minutes. Any object may be used, but something unusual will
stimulate thought and the results will be interesting.
Other objects to use as subject matter for a poem - .
Geological specimens - fossils, stones and minerals
A feather - a peacock's feather or some exotic feather
A toy plane or car or doll
An artist's brushes or palette
A floppy disk
A piece of interesting fabric or a patchwork quilt
A high heeled shoe
A large sea shell
A child's drawing
A packet of plasters
A plum
An apple or any fruit
A bunch of flowers
One perfect rose
An empty pizza box
A button

A hot water bottle. Just about anything can be used to trigger an idea for a poem.

SEAGULL
Seagull, seagull
to the mountains of wind
the turrets of air
and falls of space.
It takes you abandoned
giving, giving
your way
your life.
Charles Goate, Boundervean

FLYING HIGH
SOARING HIGH UP IN THE SKY
OVER MOUNTAINS AND VALLEYS
FLYING OVER THE OCEAN SO BLUE
HOVERING OVER FISHING BOATS
TRAWLERS TOO.
WAITING FOR DINNER
SCAVENGING ABOUT FOR
ANY BITE WILL DO.
Gary Gibson, Boundervean

EXERCISE 32

Subject: 'Colour'
Notes: Do a poem about a colour.
Think of a colour and things that might be that colour -
Red - Scarlet woman, pelagonium, rose, London bus, post-box, telephone kiosk, blood.
red admiral, red face, red alert, red traffic light - stop, red-blooded, a revolutionary, a robin red-breast, red cedar, red carpet, Red Cross, red flag, red current, red-handed.

Red-Guard, redhead, red-hot, red-herring, Red Indian, red letter
day, red meat, redneck, red rag, red pepper, in the red, red deer,
Red Planet - Mars, red tape, fire.

Blue - unclouded sky, eyes, sea, butterfly, forget-me-not,
geranium, delphinium, the blues, blue mood, bruise, air blue with
swear words, smoke, washing blue - bleach, indigo, Prussian blue,
Bluebeard, bluebell, blue blood, blue-black, bluebird, bluebottle,
blue movie, blueprint, blue-tit, blue-eyed boy, out of the blue,
blue murder, true blue.

Yellow - cowardly, buttercup. ribbon, hair, sallow, jaundiced,
yellow-cab, yellow-bellied, yellow pepper, courgette, sulphur,
primrose, egg yolk, yellow-fever, yellow-dog, Yellow Pages,
Yellowhammer. yellow peril, yellow streak.

White - white faced, egg white, cloud, sea horses, sand, clean
page, bleach, pure snow, ice berg, unblemished, virginal, white
witch - not malevolent, whitebait, whiting, polar bear, white beard,
father Christmas, white elephant, milky white, white feather, white
light, white noise, white night, white slave trade, whitewash, white
whale.

Write a poem based around a colour, getting as many colours
or shades into the poem or working on the theme of colours, or
just using something coloured in the poem, just to get you started
on an idea. It can veer off into anything else you want. The colour
is just a trigger for the idea.

THREE SHADES OF BLUE

Three shades of blue
and I'm in love with you,
over valleys of yellow
and green rolling
down so low never to be
seen. Jumping up
and down till you see
the ground seems to be
like a shade of brown. *Gary Gibson, Boundervean*

CHARLES

Charles wears three jumpers
(He gets very cold).
The top one is green, v-necked.
They are all very old, bobbly, stretched.
(He gets very attached to his jumpers).
I once bought him a new jumper
for his birthday
but I've never seen him wear it.
Heather Ashworth, Boundervean

ROYAL BLUE

Royal Blue gowns deep
mellow warm,
Escorts you to assurance, calm,
Undaunted though yielding.

Picking softly out undemanding,
Notice Royal Blue
And think again
some king capping the blue sky.
Charles Goate, Boundervean

ALL COLOUR TO THE EYE

In a blank rhythm
blanket law
stays time
lit by life
under the sun.
To its fabric
rise the awning
and adornments
of activity;
sound, motion, vision, being.

Good or evil,
it is all colour

to the eye, the mind
or heart.
Listen, the light or dark
span out and out
the colour proportion;
the darklit, the light,
are mown grass to us
as our soul mirrors.

Beneath lie in time
the touchstones,
these colours common.
And too the fountains
of silent visage existence,
imperceivable colour
conversing, evoking-.
Charles Goate, Boundervean

EXERCISE 33

Subject: Picture postcards
Notes: I keep a huge collection of old and new picture postcards
to use in workshops. It is a favourite exercise at Boundervean.
The writer chooses a card and then writes about anything that it
inspires in him or her to write.
What is it a picture of?
Is there a story within the picture?
Describe the colours and shapes and what the picture says to you.
Does it remind you of anything?

I join in the exercise if I haven't got to scribe for too many
writers. It is not always easy to come up with an idea. I never
cease to be amazed at the quality of the poems that get produced
within the workshops.

Heather chose a photo card of a nursing pig and her piglets.
Gary chose a picture post card of a Welsh landscape. Even though
he is partially sighted he enjoys these postcard exercises. He has
a great imagination. Charles' poem based on postcard of elephant
armour.

THE SIRDAR

To his aide a memo,
seeing the war elephants
on travels: an armour to Calcutta.
The beast parading power
fell to law
on a hot, dusty, day
greed of no essence but battle,
immediate and one victory alone.
Fleetingly the sirdar mused
No man, no elephant easy,
not excellence, not pride.
Law shall test endeavour's spirit;
the savages, the sirdars, an empire
Charles Goate, Boundervean

GENESIS

Oil on troubled water -
Could be a barmy interpretation
of a Rorshach test,
a flaming sunset from an erupting volcano.
Dreadful deadly sludge from a holed oil tanker.
Look on the bright side.
Could be gases from some still unborn galaxy
waiting to burst into life.
Shimmering changing shifting colours,
easy on the eye, soothing, meditative, peaceful,
swirling movement an ever-changing scene.
A careless footstep and all could be gone
the magic scattered into oily droplets.
Dorothy Biddick, Rehab Unit, City Hospital, Truro

PIGS

We were driving home from our caravanning holiday in Dorset,
when suddenly we saw the pigs at the side of the road.
The mother was huge, muddy, pink where the flesh showed
through,

and she lay on her side asleep.
She had obviously escaped from a nearby field.
Seven or eight little piglets wide awake and squealing
pulled at her teats.
Dad stopped the car,

'Look at that!' he said
'We could take one home and have it for tea. Delicious!'
'It'd last us a month.'
'No Dad, you can't,' said my little sister, who had a soft heart.
'I wouldn't eat it either,' I said firmly.
'They probably belong to someone,' said my Mum.
'We don't want a farmer following us with a shotgun.'
'No, I suppose not. Never mind then,' said Dad, and drove on.
Heather Ashworth, Boundervean

SUN SETTING
THE SUN IS SETTING IN THE
DISTANCE
BEHIND THE RUGGED
MOUNTAINS.
A SMALL SHALLOW LAKE
RUNNING BETWEEN THE
MOUNTAINS.
SHADOWS SLOWLY SHOWING UP
IN THE DARK DEEP BLUE SKIES.
YELLOW AND PINK SHINING
ACROSS THE SKY.
Gary Gibson, Boundervean

EXERCISE 34

Subject: 'If I were blind'
Notes: If you suddenly lost your sight, what would you miss?
Think of all the things you love to see –
Describe them in detail.
The sea on a wild day with white horses prancing on the dark green waves.
Kittens feeding, marching on their mother's fur. Her eyes closed in contentment.
Your baby's smile - the way your husband wrinkles his nose - bluebells thick in the dark wood.
If any of the writers are already unable to see, ask them to tell what they really miss.

IF I WERE BLIND
I would miss seeing my lovely family,
The beautiful woman;
My grandchildren the birds and the trees,
Flowers, the sea, the stars.

You could not see to read and watch television,
You could not see what you are eating.

I would not be able to see the lovely house I built
With the fantastic views.
I love going to agricultural shows to see the cattle,
Horses, all beautifully turned out.
David Wills, Rehab Unit, City Hospital, Truro

EXERCISE 35

Subject: 'Fire!'
Notes: Your house is on fire - your loved ones and pets are safe.
Your important papers like passport, insurance, etc. are safe.
You must decide what to take with you.
Six things - Anything - large or small, e.g.- a piano - remember
tunes you have played on it. Your uncle playing on it.
Your computer, but tell us how you use it. Do you email friends?
Take pearls your mother wore; books you want to read again -
what books?
Your entire 'Fifties shoe collection; Clarice Cliff jug; old buttons;
stamps;
favourite chair. Elaborate- show us why it is important to you.
Family photographs - give details and memories;
Your wine collection; records; orchids;
You can take memories - what happened in the house?
You can take a moment in time - when your wife told you she was
pregnant; when
your child was born; when you passed an exam; when you had a
letter from a long-lost friend.
Take a remembered scent - the smell of your baby's skin; apple
pie; lavender bags hanging in the wardrobe.
Take a sound - your pet dog's bark welcoming you home; the
kettle singing; the wind swishing in the bamboos.
You can take anything with you.

UPON A BURNING DECK
If a fire
felt like usurping
my place at no 49,
a)I'd be bloody annoyed
that fate had said that
was to happen.
My place at no 49
is everything there virtually;
you see, I think about the place,
HQ I call it,
have given much thought to my
life there
when Dad or my brother stays,
when friends visit or
I shut the door going out
or spend so much time with God,
or make a coffee,
go for a piss in the piss bucket
to save me going downstairs,
smoke like anything
surrounded by things I like.
When leaving, I'd take this bloody fire
and give it a watery, foamy grave
for trespass, sentenced, convicted,
furiously bloody well damned!
Charles Goate, Boundervean

IF I HAD TO LEAVE QUICKLY
I'd take my memories of the party Andy and I threw in the house
When anyone who was close to us at the time was there.
My memories of Tom and Matty growing up,
How a good day with them was a good day with the world.
The memories of Chris and Chris, both gone and both so different
But so close to both of us that we didn't need to think of them.
Claire Sexton, Rehab Unit, City Hospital

EXERCISE 36

Subject: 'And you...What should I give you?
Notes: Read some love poems including 'How do I love thee?'
Elizabeth Barrett Browning, 'Valentine' by Carol Ann Duffy,
'Meeting at Night' by Robert Browning, 'And you, Helen', by
Edward Thomas
Start a poem with the line: And you-? What should I give you.

AND YOU
And you, Nis, what should I give you?
So many things I would give you –
A Computer screen to show you the joy of this land,
Its rolling green hills, tors, cliffs and sand;
A programme to remind you
That I'm here near Land's End;
Hoping for this our love to mend;
A C-D Rom atlas to show you the way;
Wings to help you fly to me.
Martin Coade, Marie Therese Unit

TONY
And you, Tony, what should I give you?
So many things I would give you –
Roses, white, like a flock of doves,
and red, like the last colour
of the rainbow and like blood;
jonquils, a field of them like a yellow tablecloth,
and I will give you all my love.
Philippa Vinson Marie Therese House, Hayle

AND YOU, YVONNE
And you, Yvonne, what should I give you?
So many things I would give you –
An ice-blue crystal pool
In whose glassy stillness
You would glimpse your own soul,
Its sweetness, its youngness, its wholeness,
The burning sun of its pure bright zeal.
Darryl Gray, Student OT, Marie Therese Unit, Hayle

Note: I ran a creative writing workshop for several of the hospice staff on the 10th September. I also saw Gill Stillwell again and she had worked on her poem IF I COULD - a variation on the theme of the poem 'And you...what should I give you..' she knew I was doing the staff workshop and had asked if she could see me. She enjoyed making the poems and was amazed with herself, having never tried to write a poem before.

IF I COULD
If I could, I would give you time to potter with your plants,
The scarlet geraniums, the deep purple petunias, the delicate lobelias.
I would give you time to walk with me along the cliffs to the cove,
The gannets, the cormorants, the herring gulls calling us out to sea,
Where we watch the seals appear to the chug of the engine.

If I could, I would give you more time to laugh with me,
our gentle chuckle which fills me with love and warmth,
Just to spend more time together, to feel your arms around me
At the end of the day
Gill Stillwell, St Julia's Hospice

I WANT YOU TO HAVE
A mother's love,
friends who will always need you.
Kindness for all creatures
and understanding.

I want you to hear a bee buzzing,
birds singing,
the gentle sound of the sea.
To always feel warm and safe.

I want the love of God to be with you.
Marjorie Pakes, Rehab Unit, City Hospital

AND YOU BLANCHE   after Edward Thomas
And you Blanche, what should I give you?
So many things I should give you -
Time, to realise your dream,
Health and youth, to carry on.
Strength, to achieve your aims,
And I would take away your pain.
Heather Ashworth, Boundervean

IV

REMINISCING

This section is meant to be more general than calling it a specific exercise might indicate, though reminiscing is a good exercise in re-establishing memories which have fallen back in importance. Sometimes happenings from one person's past will trigger another writer's memories. Or, the benefit may not actually be in the writing, rather in the telling of it. Nevertheless the writing of it serves to provide a momento of the occasion and may result in something like a letter or footnote to 'history'.

At the Hospice I always ask if I may write down their history as they tell it to me. This gives me an idea of their interests and who or what is important to them. I find that people who are only too aware of their mortality and perhaps their imminent death, are eager to tell truths and want them to be recorded. They are getting all the medical and nursing care they need, and welcome an outsider to talk to, like me - a neutral listener - not a carer or a loved one. They welcome the opportunity to write down things they may not have had the chance to discuss with their families. I give them the time to do that. And by showing them how simple it can be to write a poem, I open up a novel way of expression. This has to done quickly because the patients usually tire easily. Intuition is needed when working in any hospital situation. Are the writers comfortable? Do they need help to sit up for a drink? Do they need a nurse? It is important to make them feel they can trust you to be aware of their needs if they are going to be able to produce a piece of writing.

I always ask if they mind if I sit on the bed, or a chair near them and I offer to scribe for them if they are too exhausted or unable to write for themselves. Everyone has different needs – a window opened or closed, a drink put to their lips. If they become emotional, let them cry, offer tissues, or offer to leave. Usually, once people start writing or telling you what they want recorded, they will not want to stop until they reach the end.
I ask ' Where do you live? .
'Have you family? Their names?

What did you do before you became ill?

This usually sparks off lots of material to work with. Older people enjoy talking about their past – their childhood – how things were when they were young.

Younger patients talk about their children or their work. To get to the heart of a person's life in a short time is important. That way you can offer them the opportunity to write about what is important to them.

A bereavement counselor once said to me that she did not think hospice patients were honest about the things they wrote in my workshops. She thought they only produced anodyne poems. I beg to differ. Several very ill people have shared the anger they feel at dying, and have produced harsh poems – see Susan Jolly's following words and the stroke unit workshop writers have produced a group moan. Most people are only too keen to remember and write about happier times.
***

SUSAN JOLLY

'I was married ten years - my married name was boring old Jenkin. I've gone back to my maiden name of Jolly. I am an unqualified homeopathist, a student still. I must do my own healing first before I can carry on studying. I really screwed up on myself - self prescribing.

I have three children: Jasmine - eleven; Aaron - eight; Dala Rose six. Jasmine is at Humphry Davy School. She went to a disco last night. Her little skinny legs and trying to keep on a pair of size five shoes that kept slipping off. Aaron said, when I asked him if he minded me having a mastectomy, 'Doesn't matter, Mummy, as long as you're alive.'

I don't know how long I've been here - a month, two months- it's a time warp. I've got some Gelipan, made from agar agar sent here from the Maudsley for my wound. Better than that honeycomb stuff which sticks to your wound and you have to dig it out each day - Ugh! I don't know how women stand it. I screamed the place down when they tried to get it off me. It was the worst thing that has happened to me here.

119

I asked her to write about one of her three children as if she were an animal or a thing. She set off dictating immediately. It was difficult to keep up with her flow of words. Her use of repetition was good and gave the poem rhythm and shape.

JASMINE
She is a soft fluffy cloud
serene, yet underneath there's
this torrent of fire.
she is a little deer that's been
frightened off into the woods
but she's strong, firm, sure,
standing there for me
despite the uncertainty
she is there for me. .

Note:I asked Susie if she could remember particular events concerning Dala and Aaron?

DARLING DALA
She started coming on the sixteenth of April
Jasmine's Birthday.
The tub wasn't ready - we made a tub
specially for Dala's birth.
My husband said: ask her to wait
and she did wait.
It was Jasmine' Birthday party.
I was looking through a red balloon -
tripping high on the labour.
This was the view Dala could see -
she could see, feel, hear, feel the sun.

AARON
He was in the womb
and I intuited that he wanted a water birth.

I was belly dancing for hours on end
I got in tune with Aaron then,

when I was giving birth
we were as one,
we were pushing as one being.
It never happened with the girls.

I gave birth at one minute to nine
the doctor hadn't come back in time,
so Nancy, my photographer friend
put her camera down
missed her last shot
and whisked him straight out of the water.
Susie Jolly, St Julia's Hospice

Notes on working in the Hospice: The work that is produced by
the hospice patients often helps give the staff an insight into their
worries and concerns and their life outside the hospice.

It is difficult to know beforehand what I am going to do with
these writers. I often see them only once or twice and have to get
to the heart of them in a very short time. What do they want of
me? Do they want me to write about their lives, their family, their
sorrow at leaving their loved ones? They usually are too weak to
write themselves and so I scribe for them. Ros was different
because she was strong enough for several sessions to write for
herself and had the energy or the necessary impulse to write.

If a patient is old I can ask them about childhood memories,
or how they met their spouse. If young, write about children,
parents and work. If unmarried, write about work or home.

I write the dictated words and shape them like a poem,
choosing line endings. When I give back the printed work I
encourage the writer to change words or shorten sentences, think
of another way of saying something if it sounds awkward. I suggest
where line endings could be improved. I point out what it is about
the work that I like and that makes it sound like a poem - e.g.
repetition, half rhymes, full rhymes, interesting imagery. I
discourage the use of clichés. The finished printed work is a
keepsake and a piece of history for them and their families and
carers

The thing is to talk first about who they are. This section of the book is devoted to those testaments or 'prose poems' which people in the Hospice created. The following are scribed for Laurence Heron.

"I have two sons - Lloyd, three and Jack, five.
Jack is a handful. He's got to that age when he knows everything.
Just started school -
St Hilary's.
Lloyd is at play school.
Batman is Lloyd's favourite character.
His Birthday is 27th September.
He'll get something to do with Batman.
Jack's Birthday is 26th March-
They both get dressed up in Batman pyjamas.
They get on most of the time.

"I met Kate through her brother, Rob.
She got Rob to go in the pub where I was drinking after work.
He asked me to come outside and meet two girls who wanted to go for a drink.
Kate and another girl.
Kate had short hair, black, straight, shaved up the back, a wedge.
We went together as friends to Margate.
That's where I asked her out.
She worked in sales.
I was labouring at the time.
Six months later she moved in with me.

"Horse-riding,
Gigging,
She does everything.
She cooks Bolognese the way I like it:
No onions
We've been together ten years.
The companionship is comforting.

"I did wood carving before this operation

Heads, ashtrays. Old wood, new wood.
If I was using old wood I'd sand it down.'
Laurence Heron, St Julia's Hospice

Note: Sometimes I choose a totally different approach with
someone who is very sick. I have to decide on the spot how to get
a result. Laurence had some interesting tattoos and I asked him
to describe them. I like the simplicity of his words – and the
poignancy of the last line. The poem tells us about the man.

MY TATTOOS
On my back a butterfly.
On my chest two swallows
done when I was fourteen.
A geisha girl,
A bird of paradise,
goblins on my left arm.
On my right hand
'Only One Life.'
Laurence Heron, St Julia's Hospice

POEMS FOR PEARL KELLY

PEARL - 'I am Pearl Kelly, called Pearly or Persil. My husband
Arthur's parents were Irish but he was born here.'

DENISE - (her daughter) 'My seven god-children call me Den
Den or Denny.'

PEARL - 'I have one boy - Paul, but he lives in Plymouth.'

If Denise was a plant
She would be a parrot plant
Always talking.
If she were a landscape -
A field full of daisies -
I could dance around her then.

If she were an animal she would be an alsation,
Strong, fearless.

If she were a type of weather
She would be a sunny day with friends.

'My friends - if I wanted anything I only have to ring up and they'd
do anything.'

DENISE and MARIE, a friend of Pearl's -
'We've had some laughs - before you were ill.'
'Coming out of Tina's, her daughter was throwing stones,
she did the splits. Wanted Pearl to do it.'
Pearl - 'I couldn't get up again.'
Marie - 'I ended up wetting myself,
Put my knickers in my pocket in the taxi.
Taxi driver said - there's a wet spot when we got out.
He asked me what we'd been drinking.
Only te!'

MARIE - 'We were going through a field, the kids on a bike,
And a horse ran after us.
She dropped the bike.
I wet myself.'

PEARL - 'We've had some fun. Oh we have!'

PEARL - 'We was up her house, Denise and me.
Marie, she was going to be sick.
I held a bowl,
Then she said she wanted a pee.
I put the bowl down there,
But it didn't go in the bowl,
It went over me.
She had a hole in her knickers.'

MARIE - 'I had migraine, didn't I!'

PEARL - 'Marie lives four doors away. Hazel, Lizzie, Diane and then Marie.
All my life I've lived in Penryn.
I used to like Newport in Wales.'

DENISE - 'Pearly is honeysuckle in a hedge.
She is pink pearl.
She is a valley with deep hills in Wales,
Houses on each hill.'

PEARL -'I want to come back as a seagull.
I could mess on all the people I don't like.'

ARTHUR - 'Pearl is a rose
A red rose that grows in the garden.
She is like the Seychelles Islands,
Low rocks, white sand, hot.
(I was on tramp steamers there,
Madagascar, South Africa,
Madras, across the Indian Ocean.)

She is like a calm day with a mackerely sky,
Flaky clouds.
She is soft and cuddly.
She makes me feel on top of the world.
We've been married 43 years.
Pearl has been tattooed on my arm for 46 years.'

VICTOR TURNER

'I was a carpenter until three years ago. I live at St Agnes Beacon - one of the highest places in Cornwall. Lovely views - I have a thirty mile view.
I have four children - Samantha, 12: Gem, 9; Victoria, 7; Joseph, 6.
Dad is called Albert. He is one of eleven, all surviving except his sister, Beatrice. She died of cancer, funnily enough. In '79 I was working at Dagenham at Fords at the time. Lovely woman, always

had children around her. she had three children, all got divorced.
Her sons got custody of the children, so Beatrice ended up bringing
up the children, virtually.
No such things as a bad child. They are all lovely. I think bullying
stems from home. They get bullied at home and take it out on
someone smaller at school.'
'I couldn't ask for better kids. If they were here now and I told them
to be quiet they would. I believe in corporal punishment. I don't
smack them often but the threat is there.
Dad and I was best friends rather that father and son. Played a
lot of golf together -in Essex. I like to think I could have been a
professional when I was young, used to beat a lot of them. It gets
hard to talk as you get older. Sometimes it's too late to express our
feeling. (Write that down. Make sure you get that down.)
My wife, Lynette is from Barking. She loves Cornwall, loves it. We
only moved here for the children. That was nine years ago. We had
two here, at Treliske. Wonderful hospital, haven't got a word to say
against it. Except ward five - about thirty patients and five nurses.
Can't get a nurse for love nor money.
I smoke too much in here, through boredom mostly and it's a
sedative.I miss dressing myself, washing myself, generally looking
after myself.'

GWEN PHEBY
'I used to play cricket for Mount Hawke Ladies,
I was Captain Wicket keeper for four or five years.
And I played hockey for St Agnes Ladies,
We played cricket against Cubert and Newlyn East,
I got a black eye there once.
I watch all sport on the tele - snooker,
rugby, cricket, soccer, and wrestling.
I don't do much wrestling any more,
only with my old man, and not so much of that lately.
We're past it now. It's not his fault.
I was post lady in Mount Hawke village for several years.
Had to carry it twice a day, two big sacks
one on each shoulder and bags to carry.

Postmen today they've got vans and sacks on wheels,
they don't know what it's like to carry post.
Got arthritis in my shoulders now because
of the wet straps, and my wrists,
and I've an under active thyroid.
My sons are Michael and Alan, daughters in law Ann and Eve.
My grandchildren are Caroline, 13, and Joanne, 26.
My husband Archie is a retired builder.
Alan has taken over the business.
Michael was a miner at South Crofty.
Twenty years ago
he was buried under rocks for three hours.

Dug him out with their bare hands.
He was stopped from falling further
by his leg which was trapped behind him.
He was only badly bruised and shocked.
It nearly killed all of us.
Directors came out from Crofty
told us he was buried up.
Someone stayed with us.
Dr Lawrence was GP for Crofty.
He said he was lucky to be alive.

Michael came back building a little bit t
then he had a heart attack.
He went to Exeter to learn woodwork -
more as a hobby to keep his mind occupied

He makes beautiful and wonderful things -
wardrobes, lamps, tables,
marvellous things he's made, beautiful.
He worked hard and played hard -
rugby, snooker, cricket, football
.

I am being spoilt rotten and I'm very lucky.

ANN, GWEN'S DAUGHTER-IN-LAW-
' We are the lucky ones.
Joanna dotes on her.
In all the years, she has never interfered,
You reap what you sow.

ME - I shall be back in a day or two.

GWEN - I shall have a zip on my mouth.

GRAHAM GRATTON
I have little to remember of my childhood. I left school at age 15
years. From that point I joined the Fleet Air Arm 9 (Royal Navy).
I was to sit an examination in these early days called NAMET.
They are basically English and Maths tests. the resulting grades
were 1.1 which is a high pass. the commanding officer asked me
what I would particularly like to do. I straight away plumbed for
air crew. This I did throughout my Fleet Air Arm career. I was
transferred to Culdrose in Cornwall on 707 squadron. The same
year, '67, we had the Torrey Canyon disaster. I had a bad
accident and ended up in hospital for six months. On release I
flew out to Singapore where I spent nearly four years. My
squadron was 848, helicopters, and were known as Her Majesty's
848 Far East taxi service. We covered most of the Far East flying
42 commando Royal Marines to wherever they had to go.

On my return to England I resigned and went to live in Israel
for two years, 70-72. I got caught up in the Yom Kippur war and
came back to England where I joined the West Midlands Fire
Service. I resigned in 1978 owing to the fireman's national strike.
From there I took up gardening where I remained until 1995
when I went off sick with sciatica and a current catalogue of
medical problems, this being the latest.

I forgot to mention that in the Fleet Air Arm another of my
jobs was air, sea rescue, where I was the winchman to hang from
the helicopter.'
Stroke Rehab Unit, City Hospital,Truro

Note: Graham had written loads more about his past, reminiscing about Jerusalem, and then about the boy scouts. I asked him to write more about the scout camps, how they won the badges. I have underlined the important words in his reminiscence to show him next time.

One writer- Marjorie Pakes, has been in hospital just over a week and is very depressed about having so many sick people around her. Linda is very ill. Jean did not come to the writing group this time but her last session 's work was given to her and she cried. She thanked me for it.

Marjorie and I went outside onto the balcony area - cleared away the full ashtray and sat at a metal table in the sunshine. Usually, I wheel the wheelchairs into a room that is crowded out with too many chairs and huge pieces of physiotherapy equipment - hoists etc. It is not the best possible space to work in. Often, a physiotherapist will interrupt the session to take out a hoist and the whole workshop comes to a halt. All the wheelchairs have to be moved to get the equipment out.

Marjorie is paralysed down one side and cannot use her hand to write but her mind is good. She enjoys reading and talking. Her husband is a retired driving instructor and comes to see her every day and walks her around the hospital grounds in her wheelchair. The wheelchairs are heavy, I found. She was upset about Linda, her bed neighbour, being so very ill. It has worried her. We talked about childhood and family. I suggested we write about family and childhood but she wanted to write about her best friend - Marj, who has the same name as her. She dictated to me:
'I was always very fit, active.
No, I didn't smoke
High blood pressure, but it was always under control.
Always checked, regularly.
The this happened.
It's such a shock.
And I find it depressing, all these sick people around me.
Linda, in the bed next to me, she was all right,
you know, talked about going home
and now she's very ill, very ill.
It's so worrying.

129

My husband - he was a driving instructor, he's retired.
He comes to see me every day, takes me out and about.
He's very good.
My daughter lives in town. She comes every day.
We are a very close family.
My mother and father, I never saw them love each other.
I was the only child but they didn't cuddle me.
People didn't in those days. Funny, isn't it?
My daughter and I do - we hold each other and cuddle.'
Marjorie Pakes, Stroke Rehab Unit, Truro.

Note: I talked to Kathleen Morris who has written her life story for her family to see when she dies. I asked if she had any memories of her children when they were little.
Her daughters are Penny and Elizabeth.
'Waiting to go into the toilet,
Penny,
vaguely knowing the word 'queue',
said,
'Hurry up Elizabeth,
there's a cucumber waiting outside.'
Kathleen Morris, St Julia's Hospice

Note: I asked Tony to write a diary poem but he preferred to try and write his thoughts about his situation so others know what he has gone through, following his accident.

TONY'S STORY
'I can remember waking up and finding myself in a strange room surrounded by beds with strange people lying in them. My first reaction was that I was still dreaming and I had yet to wake up properly.I just lay still and looked around for a short while. Then I decided to ask questions I knew that my leg was painful but I didn't know why. I got my wheelchair and asked someone who looked like they knew what was going on - it happened to be a nurse - I asked her where I was and the look on her face was saying, 'Don't you know?'

I was still convinced that I was in a dream even weeks later and I'm sure people must have thought I was mad. Even now find this a very hard situation to come to terms with as my last true memory was going to bed at home. Obviously I could read the look on people's faces when I would continue to ask them if this was a dream. I even went to the level of placing a bet with Conrad that this was a dream I was having.I now owe him a tenner but I'm sure he will let me off.

Even now I'm still asked by people, "Do you still think you are dreaming?" and the answer I say to myself very quietly is 'Yes.'

Because I'm craving for more information I'm asking as many people as I can to explain how I've got into this situation. I'm constantly nagging about being in the situation that I'm in at the moment and the condition that I am in. When I explain this to my father he says you are lucky to be alive, and started to explain to me that I had a nasty car accident, the sort that people are lucky if they are still breathing months afterwards.

I was driving a mark 2 Ford Escort which my dad had been given for a trial run. I've got no memory of this, it's just what other people have told me. Apparently I was hit from the side and managed to get the passenger side of the car coming and joining me in the driver's seat I don't know why it happened, how it happened or any of the events leading up to it.'

Note: At the next workshop I asked Tony to write about what he had lost since the accident.

'I have lost at least seven months of time and memories. For the first time I have to accept what other people tell me about events of the past.

From what people have told me it would appear that the things I've forgotten were probably best forgotten anyway.

Grief and aggravation would be the words used to explain the events that I've lost and I suppose that at this moment in time these are the memories I could quite do without.

The important things still seem to remain although they do need a dusting off - like my ability to read, walk, write, talk, breath. It sounds silly but I could easily have lost anyone of these things.

The things I have gained are probably my revised view of life and putting things in order of importance. Things that I used to take for granted I now really appreciate and other people's attitudes have no doubt changed also.

From now on I am going to take advantage of situations and make the most out of my life.'

Tony Anderson, Stroke and Brain Injury rehab unit, Truro

DAVID WILLS

'I am one of seven and we lived in a small farm cottage with a sitting room and three small bedrooms and a kitchen with an old Cornish range. My mother and my father were very poor.

It was a cottage with twenty acres of land. We had cows and three horses, a few pigs. My father would grow potatoes, cabbages and cauliflower . When the potatoes were ready for picking he used to keep us home away from school. He used to think picking potatoes was more important than going to school.

Harvest time was my favourite time of year. We would get the horses harnessed up to pull the machine. What a lovely sight.

During the end of the war food was scarce so we had ration books which was full of coupons. Fruit was a treat. I was eight years old before I even tasted a banana. Then one day we heard that bananas were in the shops, So my mum walked four miles to buy some. It was as big a treat for other people as it was for me.'

Stroke rehab unit, Truro

Childhood Memories of 'Nan Fish Shop'

The beginning of the war I was seven years old. I had whooping cough and because my mother and all the uncles worked in the wet fish trade, Nan was the one to look after me.

We called her Nan Fish Shop. Her wet fish shop was in Globe Road, Bethnal Green, and I remember so well the big white boilers in the flagged stone kitchen. The first one as you went in was kept for boiling clothes. The fire you lit under the copper. The other five were kept for boiling shrimps and crabs in. The shop had big flag stones, wood shutters and always smelt of carbolic soap cos Nan always cooked a meal every day for the whole family to have together before going their different ways. She polished the black range with a brush and buffer. I could see my face in it. She always put my hair in rags to make it curly. One job I had was to cut newspaper up in squares, thread it with string and hang it in the toilet, which was called a WC in London, meaning water closet.

Opposite was a big wooden door where Nat and Uncle Ted threaded haddocks on iron rods, which were put from wall to wall, then a special wood fire was lit and kept going all night to smoke the haddocks - proper fish, not coloured as now, and big, too.

Uncle Ted sold shellfish from a barrow Sunday mornings - he hated it. In front of the dining room sash window was a big galvanised tank in which my gran kept plaice, eels, different fish - as pets. She had a goat once, and two Alsatian dogs. My Uncle Bill made me a scooter out of fish boxes.

There was always the smell of fish..... in the shop, which my Nan scrubbed every day lived my Nan, my Mum's brother Ted, Billy, who was married to Auntie Liz and they had five children, one of which was my cousin, Joan, who also worked for the family concern, plus Bill Sharman, who was courting my Mum's youngest sister, Rose. A goat, two alsations - Peggy and Judy, and the fish in the tank outside. The connecting room between the shop and dining room had a big double bed in it. Every afternoon I was made to have a nap. Other times I opened the newspaper for the fish to be wrapped in. Sometimes I was allowed to wrap the fish up.

Every night my Granddad went for a pint in the pub which was next door but one from the shop. There was Mrs Fry's, a drapers, where I'd go to buy ribbon for my hair when Mum curled it so I'd look tidy, with a clean pinafore on etc. for when my Mum came.

The other side was a workman's cafe, next to that a pub, a bit like the one in EastEnders. I used to go with a jug and 6d in old money to get my Nan's brown ale. I'd knock on the swing doors and they 'd call my Granddad and he 'd get a jug of brown ale. I'd take it back to Nan and have a little drop in a glass - my Nan in winter used to heat a poker and stick it in her glass of beer and it would froth up. When Mum came in I used to hold her hand and pick the fish scales off which had stuck there. My uncles went every morning early to Billingsgate fish market to get the fish for the shop and also they had stalls at Erith in Kent and Dorking and there was a big market well known in the East End called the Caledonian market in Caledonian Road. My Mum 's family were well known there. I'd go with them from six weeks old. My uncles scrubbed and strengthened a fish box out, and Mum padded and lined it.

So many memories.

I slept with my Nan in a big brass headed bed.

She was a very slight lady, with jet black hair, always in a plait at night, wound round her head. She washed it twice a year and then rinsed it in beer. It shone. Although she was in her late sixties there was no grey. She used to plait it and wind it around her head. She always wore a wrapover pinafore, like my Mum, and worked from morn till night.

We used to sit outside the shop in the evenings and everyone stopped to talk to Nan. When war broke out I used to stand with my cousins and watch the dog fights between Spitfires and German planes, then collect shrapnel. My Dad was really cross so Nan stopped us.

I remember when Uncle Bill died. He was only about thirty-nine. I stood in the doorway and watched the funeral procession. I'd never seen so many flowers. He was very well liked and known. Auntie Liz was left with five children to bring up, but Nan used to have them around for meals.

I used to get shopping from a little Jewish shop for Nan. I'd get a couple of rashers, and two eggs for Granddad's breakfast, and two ounces of best butter, and two ounces of loose tea, which they did in a little bit of paper - greaseproof, which they twisted like a cone. I was fascinated. It was so dark in there but different smells pervaded the air. It was like an Aladdin's cave and I'd get change from 6d in old money. My grandparents traded under the name of Hales, but their surname was Bruton.

My Granddad was of Irish descent but Nan was of French descent. Unfortunately, the shop was bombed in the war and a block of flats now stand there. My Nan moved to Enfield in my

Aunt Rose's house and died about 1943 of cancer. She was Harriet Bruton. Granddad was Nathaniel Bruton. He died about 1939.
Pat Clark, Stroke Rehab Unit, City Hospital, Truro

LEON GUYSELMAN

Leon has been at rehabilitation for two weeks or so, after being flown home from Ecuador where he had been working in a gold mine. He is a great talker. Marjorie and I just listened.

'I have got brain damage. Can't use my left side. And I am left-handed. I am a pure-bred pedigree mongrel. I hate the French. Not keen on the Dutch. I have had three children. The first, a boy, died at three days. I can still see his face. Henry. My wife is Japanese Indian. Her name is Ogata Sang. A week ago I was a moving cabbage - scrambled too. I am a lot better now. I don't remember the accident, only what I was told about it. I don't even remember the mine inspection. I was in an explosion in a gold mine in Ecuador. An earthquake came first, caused the explosion - a little rag fell on a line of gunpowder or something like that.

I rescued a trapped man - he died later. There is a video of the accident. It was in August. A month later a heavy piece of machinery fell on me and injured my head. The vehicle that was taking me up the mountain to the hospital at Pinas went off the road and rolled down the mountainside. I had an operation in Ecuador then I was brought home. I live near Land's End.

Valerie Grace, my daughter extracts DNA at St Bartholomew's Hospital. My other son, also Henry, is 25, married and lives in London. He has a daughter, Madeleine, four years old; I call her 'trouble.'

'I'm not trouble.'

'Yes you are. You're big trouble.'

My son follows my wife's father. My boy is so easy to get on with. But if he doesn't like you...

I have been offered a job fishing and processing crabs in Newlyn Bay. When I am out of here. I've got plenty of other work to do.

When I was 21 I went to Australia - £147 it cost me. There were lots of £10 tourists, immigrants. I worked at Groote Island and Gove

in the north-east - a bauxite mine.I went to Borneo and sold cars.
I sold seventeen to the Sultan of Brunei - 17 four-door and a six-door
Mercedes and fleet of Chrysler Valients. I met my wife in Brunei
when I was in the RAF. I went to Indonesia, close to the Malaysia
border, and did timber work. Went up a river dulun - a tidal wave.
Like the Severn bore. There are seven waves one after another. Above
that the river goes as normal, below that the level is at least one
yard higher. It broke the timber rafts snapped the wires. We lost the
oil drums. We used to see the local boys surfing up the river. Very
interesting it was there. I would go back tomorrow. I saw wild
orang-utan in Borneo. I helped build roads and bridges built
without a nail. The local Ibans caught fish in the river, built the
bridges and the roads.I was a ship's cook once, local coaster 1962-3
before I went to Malaysia.I was working in Geevor Mine when I got
interested in robins.'

This robin landed on the car bonnet when I got home, to see me in.
When I got home from a shift, no matter what time.
Blackbirds and robins come to my whistle.
The robin comes into the house and feeds from my hand.
My wife has taken over
And the robin follows her indoors.
I cut good bread and cheese.
Chocolate flavoured cream biscuits of course.
You don't expect the poor little sods to eat substandard food?
The blackbird likes sweets.
The wife has got a cat now, white and grey and tinted,
I don't know its name. I must ask her its name.
We have foxes that come to the house as well as badgers.
In Ecuador I had a bat nesting in our hut.
When I whistled and called at night
the damn thing would land within a yard of me.
It was about eight inches across, with two jagged stripes.
Black with brown wings,
white zigzags going down its back.
If I was there it would be there,
if I wasn't there it wasn't to be seen.
It would answer every whistle.
Leon Guyselman, Stroke Rehab Unit, City Hospital, Truro

FRED 'S STORY

'It was a new place, new people, and it was expected to be a new experience. I had just arrived in Kalimantan to help with the management of the water supply in the town of Pelangkaraya.

The first and second days were taken up with introductions to the management and staff or the water authority and opening the company account at the local bank. It was at the bank that I met two people, one from Canada, the other from Australia, who were to play a significant part in what followed the next day.

That evening on returning to the hotel and having had a chat to the manager and owner of the Adidas I went for a walk in the town, which was quite interesting as it was the fasting period for Moslems. During this period Moslems do not eat or drink between sunrise and sunset, after which they tend to eat communally. When I returned to the hotel and after another chat with the manager at the reception desk I decided to take a small meal in the room before settling down to read the most recent report by the World Bank relating to water supply and sanitation in Central southern Kalamantan. Having read the report and by now feeling rather tired I decided it was time for bed, it being now around 11 o'clock. I must have fallen asleep almost immediately. The next thing I realised was that a peculiar feeling of not being able to rise from the bed, it appeared in the first instance to be almost dream-like and the nearest description of the feeling I had was that of a turtle or tortoise being on its back and not being able to turn over, flapping, flapping uselessly. Oh my God, what is this horror! It was at this stage that I realised what I was experiencing was in fact real and that I couldn't rise from the bed. To say that I felt panic would be an understatement as I suddenly realised that I was experiencing a stroke.

The seriousness of the situation came on me like a hammer blow. What could I do? How could I raise the alarm? I now remembered that I had locked my room and left the key in the door, could I somehow crawl to the door and at least take out the key from the lock to enable the hotel staff to get in? Having decided on this course of action I rolled off the bed and landed on my back on the floor and immediately realised that I was in a

137

worse predicament than before as I still couldn 't move but was now having to lie on a hard tiled floor. I managed to grab the telephone with my right hand from the bedside table by reaching over my head and tried calling the watchman or whoever was on duty. I also began shouting for help. Someone at last came to the door and timidly knocked to know whether I was all right. I told them as well as I could in Bahasa Indonesian that I was very sick and that they should call the manager immediately. The time of the stroke was around 2am in the morning and it was now approaching 3am and I was still lying in the same position on the floor; this was now a real nightmare and I kept begging the staff to please bring the manager immediately. Eventually the manager came and I explained to him through the locked door what had happened and that to get into the room it would probably be necessary to break down the door This is what eventually happened the time now being after 4am. The manager said he would call the local hospital and ask them to send the ambulance. However, the feeling of having made contact with people was of some considerable relief and the ambulance soon came and took me to the local hospital.

In the meantime l had implored the hotel manager to call my friend, George Meyer, who was also working on the World Bank project, but not actually involved directly with the work I was doing. He assured me he would and within another hour or so George arrived. One must realise that going into a hospital in Pelangkaraya was not quite like entering a hospital in Britain. On my arrival there was no doctor on duty and another two hours elapsed before a doctor appeared. It was a lady doctor who could speak no English and as far as I could gather, in fact, she didn't speak at all, at least not in my presence. She soon left having prescribed some medication and George was then left to arrange a suitable room where I could stay.

There apparently was only one room in the hospital that had an air conditioning unit and this was cluttered with hospital paraphernalia and had to be cleared out before the room could be used. One also has to realise that the temperature at this time was 30c with a more than 100 per cent humidity, which is extremely hot,especially if one has to stay in a small room that is not air-conditioned.George had to take the initiative and organise the few hospital staff that were there to carry out the arranging of the room and some three hours after my arrival at the hospital I was finally taken form the stretcher into a bed. However, there was something that had not been removed from the room and that was mosquitoes. There must have been thousands of them, big ugly brutes laden with blood and biting like hell. George meanwhile had gone back to his home for his wife who came to sit with me while he arranged my exit from Pelangkaraya.

However, this is another story and will be told in ensuing chapters.'
Fred Sampson, Stroke Rehab Unit

ROS WILLIAMS

Ros Williams produced about eight poems in the short time I knew her and worked with her – from December 24th to the end of January when she died. She was always keen to have homework and she found comfort in being able to express her feelings for her family. She said that her husband was particularly moved by the following poem, which she had written with no prompting from me.

I suggested she write about things lost to her. What had she lost in her life?
E.g. - friends; family; ability to do things; time. See Exercise – 'Lost and Found'

LITTLE BIRD
I wander along the leafy lane
towards the avenue of trees.
I gaze up into the clear blue sky
and see the birds gliding in the breeze.
What must it be like to be a bird
soaring to a great height
with its feathery fragile wing
catching food on its flight,
to be so small and yet so strong

139

its spirit flies free?
So when I leave this leafy lane
That little bird's spirit could be me.
Ros Williams 29.12.96
This poem was read out at her funeral at the end of January 1997

Note: Ros wanted to know what poems to read. I read to her from
Address of Paradise by Zofia Ilinska, her poems about cancer,
including 'I talk to my cancer' and 'Haikus from Hospital'.

I TALK TO MY CANCER
I talk to my cancer a lot.
Cancer, Cancer, what is this plot
to oust me from the land of living?

Enigmatic insidious
grazing on me - an ox on grass -
I imagine you spawning, spawning
thousand cells - asymmetrical pink
in each cell bloated eye - black as ink -
abstract painting by Salvador Dali...

Cancer, cancer, I deeply resent
this intrusion without my consent
brute - invader - parasite - squatter -
having forced me to dance more or less
on the tightrope between life and death
condemning me now for that matter
To this battle, this duel for life
chemotherapy - discipline - prayer -
mental use of my little black knife,
cleansing floods of luminous water
to flush out your mysterious power...

Du calme, o my soul - easy - easy
carcinomas are not for sissies...

Praise your enemies if they deserve
your respect. Praise your adversary.
Cancer, though I admit you have
half-demolished my house - can you be
some astonishing messenger from
worlds as yet not open to me?
For since you called - unforeseen
gifts are showered. How else to explain
clearness in the meaning of things
God - dream - vision - eternal city -
joy - hope - quietness - infinity
Cancer, cancer, do you hold the key?

Cancer does not answer.
Zofia Ilinska (1921-1995)

LATE FRAGMENT
And did you get what
You wanted from this life, even so?
I did.
And what did you want?
To call myself beloved, to feel myself
Beloved on the earth.
Raymond Carver (1939-1988)

141

Though this is not an index as such, I would like to offer a special thank you to all the workshop writers whose work contributed to this book –

MARIE THERESE HOUSE, ST MICHAEL'S HOSPITAL, HAYLE
Martin Coade
Darryl Gray
Cathy O'Callaher
Barbara Faragher
Jauliana Greer
Kerry Jackson
Jenny Rowe
Carol Heardson
James Lloyd Stewart
Malcolm Wilton
Paula Fowler
Gary Weaver
Anne Noonan
David Westaway
Anne Mackay
Philippa Vinson

BOUNDERVEAN
Gary Gibson
Mary Phillips
Shirlie Lillie
Charles Goate
Barry Shaw
Heather Ashworth
Diana Humphrey-Snow

ST JULIA'S HOSPICE
Kathleen Morris
Cathy Davey
Anne Blake
Jenny Rickard
Rosemary Bottrell
Johnny Bottrell

Susan Jolly
Teresa Finnegan
Gwen Pheby
Donald Nancarrow
Pearl Kelly
Rosalyn Williams
Victor Turner
Ivy Claydon
Steve Stephens
Brian Stevens
Gill Stillwell
Elizabeth Parry
Laurence Heron

STROKE AND BRAIN INJURY REHABILITATION UNIT, CITY
HOSPITAL, TRURO
Jeanette Thomas
Nyall Thomas
Leon Guyselman
Janet Creddy
Chris Pearson
Roy Glanville
Graham Gratton
Mel Landsbury
Dorothy Biddick
Peter Kemp
Pat Clark
Fred Sampson
Charles Shone
Tony Anderson
Marjorie Pakes
Paul Hoskin
Claire Sexton
David Wills
And all other patients and carers who took part in the workshops

SUGGESTED READING

Curtis, Tony, Ed. *How Poets Work*, Seren, ISBN 1 85411 1310

Fox, John, *Poetic Medicine*, Jeremy Tarcher/Putnam, New York, ISBN 0 87477 882 4

Gittins, Chrissie, Ed. *'Somebody Said That Word' Living in a hospice*, Littlewood Arc, The Nanholme Centre, Shaw Wood Rd. Todmorden, Lancs, OL14 6DA

Goldberg, Natalie, Writing Down the Bones, Shambahla, ISBN 0 87773 375 9

Hynes, Arleen McCarty, and Mary Hynes-Berry, *Biblio/Poetry Therapy: the Interactive Process*, North Star Press, 1986

Killick, John, *Please Give Me Back My Personality! Writing and Dementia,* Dementia Services Development Centre, University of Stirling, Stirling FK9 4LA Scotland

Samson, Fiona, *Writing as a Healing Art*, Hospital Arts, Isle of Wight, Hampshire

Stillman, France, *The Poet's Manual and Rhyming Dictionary*, Thames and Hudson, ISBN 0 500 27030 9

POEMS

Albery, Nicholas, Ed. *Poem for the Day*, Sinclair Stevenson, ISBN 1 85619 499 X

Benson, Gerard, Judith Cherniak, and Cicily Herbert, Eds, *Poems on the Underground*, Cassell, ISBN 0 304 34858 9

Carver, Raymond, *All of Us, The Collected Poems*, The Harville Press, ISBN 1 86046 364 9

Gibson, Ewan, Aine Jackson and Christopher Pillow, Compilers, *Lifelines Two*, Town House, Dublin, ISBN 0 948524 76 6

Herbert, Cicily and W. E. Henley, *In Hospital*, Katabasis, ISBN 0 904872 19 X

Illinska, Zofia, *Address of Paradise*, Tabb House, Padstow, ISBN 1 873 951 31 0

Monagle, Mac, Ed. Lifelines, Town House, Dublin, ISBN 0 948524 46 4